Addiction,

Depression,

Mushrooms,

And Me.

"How I Got Sober
with Psilocybin Mushrooms"

By Myles Bradley

ISBN: 978-1-7779363-0-3

Addiction,

Depression,

Mushrooms,

And Me.

For Dalton

and

anyone suffering.

Psychedelic:

From the ancient Greek word psyche (for mind, soul) and deloun (to make visible or reveal)

"To hell or soar angelic / Just take a pinch of psychedelic".

Humphrey Osmond to Aldous Huxley.

Addiction, Depression, Mushrooms and Me

Table of Contents

Introduction.

I crashed my car, killed my eight-year-old son, and I almost died. Before that day, I was a chronic pothead/alcoholic, and after that day I was even worse. I was stoned every minute of every day for the next fourteen years. I lived most of my life with addiction, depression, and after the accident, PTSD. I carried the guilt and remorse of my dead son like a thousand-pound boulder. If you are hurting, suffering, or struggling with addiction, you might be interested in what I have to say. When I thought that killing myself was the only way to find relief, I had to eat a bag full of psychedelic mushrooms to get clean, sober, and comfortable with life. What I learned was so profound, so life-changing, and so lifesaving, but it went against society's norms, it went against the establishment, and it went against everything I thought I knew.

Let me start by saying I am not a doctor; I am not a psychiatrist, a pharmacist, a chemist, a biologist, or a mycologist. I have always wanted to get clean and sober but was never able to. I tried many avenues to quit, including rehab, psychiatrists, cold turkey, hypnosis, psychotherapy, and anti-depressants, but nothing ever worked for me. That was until one day I stumbled upon the easiest way to get clean and sober, and it was right there in front of me the whole time, but who knew? Oh, they knew.

I'm talking about psychedelics, specifically, psilocybin mushrooms, more commonly referred to as 'Magic Mushrooms.' You might consider this fiction or conspiracy. You might think this a self-help book, but whatever you consider this, it is my story of struggling with addiction and depression and how mushrooms saved my life and helped me get sober. What I'm going to discuss might help you, it might not, it might educate you, and it might urge you to go on your own journey to see if mushrooms can help you with whatever your struggle is. I will explain my history of addiction from a teenager, how I struggled with depression my whole life and how PTSD stifled and muted my life for years. I will also explain how I was able to break free from all of that with Psilocybin Mushrooms. This book is not intended to be a how-to book; this isn't a recipe for quitting, but it might be. Instead, I want to share with you what I learned about mushrooms, how they helped me and how they might be able to help you. But the mushroom may not be for everyone; this is my story of the addiction, the depression, the doctors, the prescriptions, the sadness, the years wasted, and how I broke free from them all using psilocybin mushrooms.

When I learned of using psychedelics for addiction and depression therapy, I went down the rabbit hole (sound familiar?). I spent a year of my life researching, discovering, absorbing, and learning everything I could about Mushrooms and psychedelics for addiction and depression therapy. I checked out every book I could find from the library, I watched every documentary I could, and I listened or watched every TedTalk or podcast on the subject. I read university papers, Scientific Journals, Congressional Hearing Reports, and even army reports, yes, even army reports. I researched and followed what the experts were saying about them. I also became a psychedelic stock investor and became an amateur mycologist, growing a couple of batches of mushrooms myself.

As of the date of publishing this book, Psilocybin Mushrooms are illegal (though they are in the process of being legalized everywhere), therefor this book and the mushroom may not be for you, but they were for me. This book is my story of what I learned about macro and micro-dosing psilocybin, the history of why psychedelics were made illegal, and why they were stigmatized. I want to share it because not only was I amazed, I was also pissed off. I was amazed at how easy it was to get sober and chase away my depression using the mushroom, but I was more pissed off that this was not discussed and talked about in the medical and scientific communities. I was pissed off about the lies the Government told us about this naturally occurring fungus that had such healing potential, and I was pissed off about how they hid it away from us for so many years. Where was this twenty years ago for me? Why did they hide it when it could have saved me and many others from going through years and years of pain and sadness?

My name is Myles, and I am forty-six years old. I have suffered from depression and addiction my whole life and suffered from PTSD since my early thirties. I started drinking at the age of twelve, began smoking cigarettes when I was thirteen and started smoking pot at fourteen. I have been constantly stoned for the last fourteen years of my life after a car accident at thirty-two years old that left me suffering from PTSD. I dabbled with cocaine and pills on and off for my whole life, and I would try anything once. I always had to alter my state of mind through drugs and alcohol, but it was marijuana that was always there for me. My whole life, I always thought I couldn't or shouldn't live without pot. I was consumed with it, I always thought I needed to be high to get by, but that was until I treated myself with psychedelics, particularly psilocybin.

I was adopted and have one brother that I never had anything in common with except our parents. I have yet to marry, which at this age means I probably never will. My first and only son died in a horrific car accident when I was thirty-two years old and when he was the precious age of eight. I have had three careers throughout my life, and I am on my fourth. I started in retail and rose to upper management; then, because of life circumstances, I became a mailman at the Post Office. After my car accident, I was forced into being a supervisor. After that, I became a commissioned sales rep in a Law Office, executing high-level sales with Fortune Five Hundred companies, and from there, I became an actor. I'm currently a starving artist trying to make it. I have never been arrested, I vote, I pay my taxes, I visit my divorced elderly parents as much as I can, and I help them with their groceries and errands. I may have made some mistakes in my life, but when I made those mistakes, I wasn't my true self. I was living my life under a 'dark cloud,' a haze or fog of addiction and depression that never really let me be me.

I'm not here to burden you with the details of my life. I'm not here to diagnose my addiction, my depression, or my PTSD or to try to figure out why I suffer from these. You may or may not relate to my reasons, and I may not relate to yours, so I will not talk about them in complete detail. I'll only speak of my life in general about addiction and depression, and I'll discuss life experiences that we all experience, but I won't be dissecting them as I don't want to bore you. I will just talk about life events and how they would send me into depression and further feed my addictions. I'll explain how I thought being depressed was expected and how I thought feeding my habits would help me get through tough times. I will also explain, how after treating myself with mushrooms, I can deal with my PTSD and deal with troubling life events without suffering from depression or running to my addictions.

Since my addictions and attempts to quit span over a time of thirty years, I'm not going to speak in chronological order. I mean, alcohol and marijuana have been a constant in my life from the age of twelve, with some moments of sobriety that would never last. I have tried to break free from substance abuse many ways and many different times over three decades. Alcohol was always around. Sometimes I'd be binge drinking for periods, sometimes I would be sober for some periods, and sometimes it would be constant and daily. Harder drugs such as cocaine, opioids, Ecstasy, and MDMA would come and go, but marijuana and depression were always with me. In hindsight, I would always be addicted to one thing or another at any given time.

I was always looking for ways to break free, ways to break the chains of addiction and the anchor of depression. I tried everything that was recommended to me and even some things that weren't. I tried natural fixes and pharmaceutical remedies, but nothing ever worked. When I first heard of psychedelic treatment for depression and addiction, it was in a casual conversation, I was surprised, and I didn't think much of it at the time. But ultimately, it was that conversation in passing that would set me free and save my life.

The road to my consciousness was presented to me about six months before I determined I needed to change my life. Since I had tried so many ways to get sober in the past, I was trying to think of how I would try to quit this time, and I thought back to that conversation about psychedelic therapy. A few months before I decided to quit, I went to see my friend perform at a comedy club. One of the other comedians was a dude named Manolis Zontanos. We had worked together once or twice on the odd TV set doing background (being an extra). When I saw him at the club, I bought him a beer and went backstage to say 'hi', to him after his set. When I offered him the beer, he said, "thanks, but no thanks, I don't drink", which was cool with me, but a little surprising. We started talking a little about addiction and comedy, which led to talking about depression and comedy because, I'm not sure if you are aware, but funny people go to some dark places in their minds. He brought up the subject of micro-dosing mushrooms or LSD to help with depression. Psychedelic therapy was new to me, and I never heard anything about this before. When I asked him, "well, what if you do too much?". In true comedic fashion, his reply was, "well then, you're just doing drugs, and I hope you don't have plans for the day!". That made me laugh, but he explained, "look, you're only doing .1 - .2 grams every other day, so even if you do take too much, you're only taking .05 - .10 of a gram more, which isn't going to have any trippy effects on you, maybe you'll just smile a little more that day, but that's it". When I remembered what he said, I decided to research it a little bit and ended up going down that rabbit hole. In hindsight, it was one of the most important conversations I would ever have in my life, and I wish I acted on it that day, but as they say, timing is everything. That conversation saved my life, and I want to thank Manolis Zontanos for it. Thank you, and peace to you brother.

At forty-six years old, I figured this would be my last 'kick at the can' to find sobriety, so I decided to learn about psychedelic therapy before going to my family doctor for help. When I went online to research and read about addiction therapy, I came across a book by Michael Pollan called 'How to Change Your Mind.' I didn't think I knew of Michael Pollan, but I realized he was the author of 'Food Inc'. I never read the book, but I loved the documentary. I went to the library and checked out his book and the audiobook (sorry, I didn't purchase it at the time, Mr. Pollan, but it is now sitting on my shelf). I was blown away! I was so intrigued, and he was so honest in his findings that it was my inspiration for learning, and I haven't been that inspired for years. My story, and my writings, are a homage to him. I also want to thank him for his work and for sending me down the path to freedom. Everything I learned, everything I did, everything I'm going to write was inspired by him. If you can relate to my story and want to go down the mushroom road, 'How to Change Your Mind' should be the first book you purchase. Thank you, Mr. Pollan.

Even though I was a 'rabid' substance abuser and addict, I had the same view and general knowledge of psychedelics as the rest of the general population. My thoughts were, *"No way, man.. I'm not messing with that kind of stuff; those things will mess you up"*. Meanwhile, I wouldn't think twice about drinking a bottle of vodka, doing a gram of coke, or grabbing some pills, but psychedelics? No way, I'm too old for that, wow was I so wrong. I used to think I was more woke or more enlightened cause I smoked pot instead of being an alcoholic. I believed pot was more spiritually freeing; I believed alcohol trapped and addicted people more and that pot wasn't addictive. Even though it wasn't physically addictive, the numbness and sedative features of pot addicted me psychologically. I looked down on alcoholics. I felt sorry and took pity on them because they needed to drink every day. I could never see a comparison between them and myself, even though I needed to smoke and be high every minute of every day. I never thought being a chronic daily pothead was anything like being an alcoholic. I believed I was nothing like them. But what I would later learn, these were all preconceived perceptions that society and the Government instilled in me, and they were all wrong.

Also, the actual name isn't 'Magic Mushrooms.' They were inaccurately named 'Magic Mushrooms' when first realized and introduced to North American society by Life magazine in nineteen fifty-seven[1]. Other ancient and modern cultures refer to them as 'the

---

[1] 'Seeking the Magic Mushroom' Life Magazine, 1957

18

flesh of the Gods'. I believe the name 'Magic Mushrooms' does them a disservice. There is nothing magical about them; it is the exact opposite. Mushrooms are a scientific and biological fact; this is mother nature and biology at its best. I believe the name discourages and scares people from knowing they are such a beneficial substance. Magic instills a mysterious or unknown power, when in fact, its chemical makeup and influence on the brain is a scientific biological fact. Therefore, I will refer to them as 'the mushroom' from here on out and out of respect to them.

Since I have opened my mind, I am amazed at how much of a difference it has made in my day-to-day life. Not only with addiction, but with my mind, it is no longer consumed with thinking of getting high or dumbing down; it has also helped with my depression and thought process. When presented with difficult situations or confrontations, my mind used to be filled with hesitation, doubt, anger, resentment, and a bevy of other negative emotions. I would dwell over past incidences and negativity, and now my mind is filled with the exact opposite thoughts, positive thoughts. My thought process is the exact opposite of what it was before, and it is astonishing. I even catch myself observing and reflecting on my inner thoughts and laughing about how my mind has changed. The way my mind goes to the exact opposite views is quite remarkable. Before there was no tolerance, there is now patience, where there was anger, there is now happiness, where there was no understanding, there is now empathy, and where there was negativity, there is now positivity.

Hopefully, it's not too late for you. Use this information to help you make your own decision. Shake your head and laugh at all the weird ways I've tried to get sober. Take the information I have learned about the 'the mushroom' and how our society and government view 'the mushroom' and demonize(d) 'the mushroom.' Learn how the medical community and doctors believed in the healing power of 'the mushroom' until the Government wrongly and criminally placed them on Schedule 1 of the Controlled Substance, along with drugs like heroin. Take this information and ask yourself, why did this happen? Who was behind it? Ask yourself, why were all psychological treatment experiments ceased at that time, and was the Government acting in our, the people, best interests? I have listed everything I have read, listened to, or watched at the end of this book. So please, read different books, listen to lectures, watch videos, read journals and scientific papers, learn everything you can and draw your conclusion. Take what I have learned about psychedelics and go on your learning adventure. I guarantee you your mind will be blown away even before you eat any mushrooms.

Disclaimer:

Remember, I am not a doctor. **If you suffer from addiction and depression, and if it is an emergency or thinking of suicide, please call 911 and seek medical help immediately.** If you think suicide is the answer, which it is not, I ask you to try psychedelics or psilocybin once before you make any attempts. Chances are you will see life in a whole new light, and you will change your mind! **(If it doesn't work for you, please, please call 911 and seek help, the world is never as bad as our minds make us think it is).** Micro-dosing (and a couple of macro doses) worked for me, but it may not work for everyone. I spoke to naturopaths, doctors, psychiatrists, psychologists, and even hypnotists and people on the internet. I did not go into this psychedelic treatment lightly or unprepared. I learned all I could and made an informed, educated decision to treat myself with psychedelics. I tried all the avenues recommended to me by my doctors over the years, but nothing worked for me. That's why I went, or should I say, I had to go down the Psilocybin Mushroom rabbit hole to find out for myself, but more importantly, to find myself.

Addiction.

All my life, I have always felt like I needed to alter my mind. I have always had the feeling that I had to be high or under the influence of something. As a child, I was addicted to sugar and would do anything to get it. I craved and loved the stuff. In retrospect, this was my first addiction, and it started when I was a young child. When I couldn't get it, I would think about it all the time. My addictions would continue into adulthood; only instead of sugar, they would be alcohol, marijuana, hard drugs and anything that would give me a buzz and make me feel good. The thoughts of getting high were constant and consumed part of my mind constantly. I started smoking pot at a young age and started drinking at an even younger age, and I wouldn't stop until I was forty-six years old.

I remember the first few times I got drunk; they were genuinely memorable moments. The first time was when I was twelve years old. My family was visiting my mom's sister in the country. When we got there, my fourteen-year-old cousin, who had a dirt bike, took me for a ride into the woods. Before we left, everyone said, "be careful, or you'll end up in the ditch." So sandy drove us directly to a bootlegger in the woods, where he bought some beer, and we proceeded to get drunk in the woods! Being so young, I got so drunk I could hardly stand. When we started to drive back, I fell off the bike three times, and just when we were close to home, Sandy crashed the bike into the ditch. When we came stumbling back and walking the bike, my parents had a look on their face like I had committed the biggest crime of the century; they couldn't believe that I had gotten drunk that young. The next time was when I was thirteen years old. I was at a sleepover at my friends' place, and his parents had gone away for the weekend.

We had found his dad's bar and proceeded to drink a bottle of 'Johnny Walker Red' between the two of us. We were young, and we thought this would be a good idea; we made macaroni and cheese for dinner then hit the bottle. We got so hammered that we put on his dad's plush polo bathrobes and were dancing around to Marvin Gaye's 'I Heard It Through the Grapevine.' By the end of the night, I was bent over the bathtub throwing up the macaroni and cheese we had made for dinner. I will never forget scooping macaroni out of the tub with my hands and putting it in the toilet. Why I didn't just throw up in the toilet, I have no idea, but to my credit, it was only my second time being drunk, but it wouldn't be my last, by far. The following day, we woke up feeling horrible and went home. We thought we got away with it until his dad called my parents and complained about the vomit all over his robe and the macaroni in the pockets.

The next time I got drunk, I was thirteen, which would be the official beginning of my drinking career. It was my baseball team's first tournament on the road in Niagara Falls. It was a three-day tournament, and we got to stay in a motel. The parents were staying in their rooms, and the kids were bunking up together in their own rooms; it was our first taste of a bit of freedom. So, what did we decide we were going to do? Well, we decided we needed to get drunk. I told my teammates that I would be able to get the booze since I was the one who came up with the idea in the first place. I stood outside a liquor store asking people to buy me some peach schnapps. After standing there for about two hours, I got lucky, and a rocker guy from the neighborhood came along. He laughed at my order but obliged and came out with two bottles of 'Dr. McGillicuddy's' Peach Schnapps. Yup, we were hardcore. But before I left for the tournament, my mom picked up my suitcase and she thought it felt heavy, so she opened my bag and went through it (she was like that) and found the bottles. When I showed up without them, the guys were disappointed, but being one not to be beaten, I told them not to worry, we'll get booze somehow.

When we got to the motel in Niagara Falls, me and a teammate went across the street from our hotel to try to get some alcohol. We stood outside for about ten minutes before someone agreed to buy us some booze (apparently, people were a lot cooler in Niagara Falls); we gave him a whack of cash. He came back with a cart full of coolers. We had to push the cart to the back of the motel through mud and tall grass and sneak it in through our bathroom window, so the parents didn't see what we were doing. We drank into the morning, and we got so drunk we even shaved one of the guys' eyebrows off. We didn't get caught that night, but the following day we were a mess. The entire team was hungover, and we ended up losing eight to zero; a couple of guys even puked on the field! That's when we got caught, and the parents were pissed off.

From that time on, drinking would be my youth. Whenever I got caught, my parents would ask me, "who put you up to this? Whose idea was this?" Nine times out of ten, it was my idea, and when I told them it was my idea, they wouldn't believe me, well at least my mom wouldn't, but my dad would look at me and just shake his head, knowing damn well it was me. My mom was so shattered that she didn't want to believe it and was convinced I was covering for someone. It was funny; every time I got caught and said it was my idea, she would just say I was lying, even when I was telling the truth, she would just tell me I was lying, so I figured, what good was there in ever telling her the truth?

I lived to binge drink on the weekends, and blackouts weren't that uncommon. Friday and Saturday nights were for getting fucked up. When I started drinking, alcohol was socially acceptable, not for my age, but people weren't too worried about underage drinking. But pot was unacceptable and was living in the shadows, and it had a real stigma; back then, pot was evil. During the eighties, you had to be hush-hush about smoking pot, and you had to be sneaky to find it. Society fell for and believed the ideology that if you used marijuana, you were the dope. They lied to us and convinced us that pot was wrong; they said pot was the 'gateway drug'. They claimed that smoking pot would lead to harder and more dangerous drugs like mushrooms, acid, cocaine, and even heroin. But later in life, I would learn that alcohol was the 'gateway drug', the drug that was legal and more socially acceptable, the drug that was way more toxic and dangerous than pot ever was. We all know that when we drink, our inhibitions go away. I don't know about you, but when I drink, mine go away. We all know the phrase, "here hold my beer" before someone does something stupid, it's not, "here hold my joint!". It's like if guys were up at a lake and you came upon a cliff, the guy with the beer would say, "here, hold my drink" just before jumping off, the guy with the joint would just say, "no, it's cool." Same way with hard drugs. Whenever hard drugs were pushed in my face when I was drunk, I would say sure, of course, I want to try cocaine. But with pot, someone asks you to try cocaine, just like the cliff, you would say, "no, it's cool," and then you would just go look for the nearest Krispy Kreme donut shop.

My next addiction was cigarettes; I remember the first time I smoked. I was thirteen and hanging out with an older kid from the neighborhood at the schoolyard across the street from my house. He had a pack of 'Vantages'; I remember the brand because the package had a cool bullseye symbol. He was smoking and dared me to smoke one; he didn't think I would, but I was never one to back down from a bet or dare, so I grabbed one and lit up. I coughed hard, and I still remember how dizzy my head was; it was as if the world was spinning. I kept smoking it, and I remember how my body tingled when I inhaled; again, I was hooked and loved it.

Then there was marijuana; besides cigarettes, it would be my best friend in the world, always there, never letting me down. I discovered it when I was fourteen, and it would never leave me until I was forty-six years old. Oddly enough, I wasn't the instigator for smoking pot the first time. It was grade eight, and my buddy (the same guy whose dad's robe I threw up on) was dating a Filipino cutie by the name of Simonetta; she didn't go to our school but went to a private Catholic girls' school. She was so beautiful, and her Pilipino friends were just as cute. One night they all said they wanted to try smoking pot, and of course, I wanted to try getting high too, so I was into it. After a bit of discussion, it was determined, none of us knew where to get some.

Wanting to be the hero to impress the girls, I exclaimed, "I'll get the pot." So, we all agreed that the following Saturday would be the night. We would get the pot and meet the girls at Simonetta's house. Christina was the cutie I liked, and she said how much she was looking forward to me and the pot, so now I definitely had to find some. I was looking forward to the following Saturday night, but I wasn't looking forward to figuring out where to buy pot. I had no clue of who to ask, what to do, or where to go. But I was so overtaken by the need to impress the girls and be the hero that I didn't care what I had to do. That day, I also realized that there were other gateways to drugs and alcohol, other gateways more powerful than booze; that gateway was women. I mean, these girls were so cute that if they asked me to shoot heroin and steal a car for them, I probably would have, hands down!

I had one week to score some pot, and there was no way I was going to let the girls down. But who was I going to ask? I was in grade eight, and nobody was smoking pot yet at my junior school; apparently, we would be the first ones. I had an older brother, but he didn't know anything about pot. I played baseball, and sometimes older guys were hanging around, and it always smelled like a skunk was on fire when they were around; they might know, shit, where do I find pot?

I remember a guy at school saying his sister would sometimes go downtown to 'score' pot; he remembered her saying that she would go to the St. Charles Tavern. Now, everyone knew about the St. Charles Tavern. It was one of Toronto's oldest bars, and it had turned into a 'dive' bar, like a bar you would see in the movie 'Roadhouse' with Patrick Swayze before he cleaned it up. It was rememberable because it had a clock tower on it that was a city landmark and that it was also one of Toronto's most notorious bars. It was on a stretch of Yonge Street with adult theatres, arcades, shady donut shops, and at night, even some hookers. It was always in the news for harboring fugitives, fights breaking out, and even drug raids. I'm sure we would find pot there.

So, one day after school, me and the buddy with the sister, Mark, headed downtown. I'll never forget how dark and seedy it looked when we walked in. It was right out of a movie; back then, you could still smoke inside, and there was a haze of cigarette smoke filling the room. Mark had balls, he walked right up to a table with two adults sitting at it. I only remember the one guy because he looked like a cowboy, he was wearing jeans, a plaid shirt, cowboy hat, cowboy boots, had a mustache, and was smoking, he looked like the Marlboro Man, I remembered him because of that and the fact that he was the one that sold us the pot.

I couldn't believe Mark; he walked right up to them and asked, "I'm looking to buy some pot, and I'm hoping one of you guys can help us out?" Damn, Mark was a pro! These guys looked at him as if he was a regular customer and said, "how much do you want?' Mark replied, "not a lot, maybe twenty, thirty dollars-worth" (we had no idea how much that would get us). The cowboy looked at Mark, then looked at me. Then he swung one leg up on the table. "I only have forty-dollars-worth, and I think you should buy it all." We hurriedly nodded and agreed, as we scrambled to get our money together, he reached into his boot and pulled a knife and said, "here's my pot, you boys trying to fuck me up? Am I going to sell you boys some pot, and then some parents or cops come down here, fucking with me? Asking me why I sold their kids some pot?" We froze. I almost pissed my pants, even though these guys looked rough, I thought they looked cool enough to sell us some pot, not fucking rob us. Mark started to reply, "no way man, we just…". The guy cuts Mark off and says, "not you" and looks right at me, "quiet guy, why you want this pot? You going to mess me up?" I looked at Mark, and I looked around the room, looking at the ground, nervous as hell, I just said, "there are some girls, they want to get high, and we want to get high with them, so we said we'd get the pot, we didn't know where to go, so we came here, thinking we could…". "Ok, Ok," he said laughing. He slipped the knife back in his boot and raised the other leg, he reached in, and this time he pulled out a bag of pot. He tore it in half and tied half of it up for us. "Hahaha, here you go, boys, be careful of what girls ask for, don't let women be your gateway to hell!" (Many years would pass, and I would sometimes often regret not listening to the wise drug dealer with a knife in his boot about women). God damn it.

I gave him the forty dollars, all the money we had, and he gave me what we were hoping was forty dollars-worth of marijuana. We were so scared we thought we were going to be arrested as we left the bar. When we left the bar and swung the doors open to the street, the sunlight hit us like a wall and blinded us. Once we left the bar, we couldn't see anything or anyone; we were blind and scared as hell. We walked through an alley on the way to the subway, opened the saran wrap, and looked inside. "Is it pot?" I had no idea how it was supposed to look. Mark replied, "yeah, yeah, it is, look at all the stems and seeds in it, that means its good pot," ah youth, so naïve. I'll never forget that experience. You would think the knife in the boot would be enough to scare two kids off pot and make them never want to try pot again? Nope! And of the hundreds, should I say thousands of times I have bought pot over my life, I have never come across a guy with a knife in his boot again. That night with the pot and the girls was fantastic. I remember being high and naked with someone for the first time; that night, I fell in love with women and marijuana. I was hooked; could you blame me? Ever since then, or should I just say forever, I have been a chronic pot user.

I was a very hyper child. I had a lot of energy, and my mind was always racing. I suffered from ADHD but was never really diagnosed. My diagnosis was just being yelled at throughout my childhood for having too much energy. I could never focus, and my attention couldn't last long at all. In school, I couldn't sit still, I couldn't sit through an entire class, and I downright hated it. I started buying pot regularly in high school. I remember walking to school in the morning smoking a joint along the way; at lunch, we would smoke a joint, and if I had a spare class in the day, I'd find someone to get high with me. I was never happy in school, and I didn't enjoy it, so I guess I had to numb myself down; they call it self-medicating, I guess I was, but I would never admit it, I always felt there was nothing wrong with me. Through high school, college, and all my jobs, every day would be wake and bake, and my days would be filled with pot. Pot was always there for me, my best friend, morning, noon, and night.

While I tried to quit many times throughout my life, it would always be short-lived; I would always run back to it and continue smoking pot. I was what you would call a high-functioning alcoholic/drug addict. In school, at work, and in life, I would do just enough to get by. My decisions were always made under the influence of something, whether it be alcohol or marijuana. Most of the money I ever earned went toward drugs; my main priority was to make sure I had pot and that I would never run out. When I was broke and didn't have any money, if the choice was food or pot, pot always came first. It was constantly on my mind, and I always wanted to be stoned. It was my excuse if I didn't succeed or didn't excel at something; I could always say, well, it doesn't matter; if I wasn't high, I would have done better; it was my excuse to fail.

I was twenty-three years old when my son was born. He was born out of wedlock and out of love. His mom wanted a baby; her life was so empty she thought it would bring her meaning and purpose; she wanted a baby, a paycheck, and nothing to do with me. From the day he was born, we were in court; she put me through utter hell, I was struggling to survive, and when I finally landed a job with some potential, she came at me with all the power of the family court system. She took me for everything I had and everything I would ever have. Up until my son was born, pot was a way-out, a way not to deal with my head; after he was born, it was a necessity. I had hoped to get sober when my son was born; I didn't want to be stoned all the time. But the situation with his mom was too much to handle. The only way I could deal with the stress of work, family court, and constantly fighting with the mom was to keep smoking pot and numb myself down. I was disappointed with myself for having a child out of wedlock, especially having a child with a woman like that, a selfish, unloving, and downright mean woman. So being constantly stoned was the only way I could cope. The only time I wasn't stoned was when I was with my son on the weekends; it seemed as if my mind was calm and happy when he was near me. But as soon as I would take him home and drop him off, I would spark up a joint as quickly as possible to stop the pain of saying goodbye to him.

When he was born, I was in my first career working in retail. I rose through the ranks to upper management at a young age; I was stoned every minute and drinking like a fish constantly. I handled the pressure and the long grueling hours because I believed in the motto, 'work hard, play hard.' My twenties were filled with nicotine, caffeine, marijuana, alcohol, and hard drugs. Family, friends, and co-workers could never tell when I was high because I was always high. I excelled at my job, and I usually outperformed and was promoted before others with more experience or seniority. I got along with everybody, and even though I was stoned most of the time, I had more energy than most people. As long as I was stoned, I could work long hours and stay positive.

Family court and working sixty seventy hours took its toll on me (more about that in the next chapter, Depression). So, after my career in retail, I took some time off to figure out how I would survive in this world with a child, fighting with his mom, and a family court system that hated me. I had decided to work at the Post Office. I became a mailman, so I would have no responsibility; all I would have to do was deliver my route, and I would be done for the day; I had no work to take home, no reports to file, no resumes to review, nothing. The minute my mailbag was empty was the minute I was done and free to go home, which meant on weekends, I had the time to go and see my son and never be late to pick him up.

When I started working at the post office, I started drinking and smoking a lot more. It was a very monotonous job; walking up and down the same street every day numbs your brain, so you need to 'numb' it further just to deal with the numbness; there is no challenge, and you don't have to think about anything. We would strap bags to ourselves, fill it up with paper, and walk up and down the same streets, we called ourselves 'Government Mules', just like the band. I would have never taken the job at the post office if it wasn't for my son, and I regretted taking the job (I still do, to this day). I'm not sure what picture of the post office you have in your head, but I don't think it's what most people think it is. It's filled with alcoholics, drug addicts, criminals, bikers, partiers, and the odd quiet average person, but most aren't normal. Don't get me wrong, it can be an excellent job for some, steady pay, good benefits, but it wasn't for me, and I had to be stoned every minute I was there. There were so many people like me working there, guys that were stuck there. Some guys were divorced, once, twice, and even three times, guys that had one, two, even three kids and financial commitments that locked them in there forever, giving them no choice in life. That kind of situation breeds addiction and substance abuse. It was constantly marijuana, sugar, binge eating at nights, and binge drinking on the weekends. I could never work when I was hungover, so I saved my drinking for Friday and Saturday nights but weeknights, was junk food, sugar, and marijuana. I would drink so much pop and eat so much candy that I would make my brain tingle like it was on cocaine. People would ask me, "wasn't working at the post office a good job?" I would joke and tell them, "Yes, it was great; I would go home and cry into my bag of skittles every night."

It was when I was at the post office that I started doing cocaine more often. Shifts at the post office can begin at any time of day two, three, four, five am, it was insane, and when shifts would start in the middle of the night, sometimes the night before would continue into the morning. A couple of the guys would be doing blow the night before, and they would just keep the party going into the morning. It was amazing how fast you'd be able to deliver your route while on cocaine. It might be a surprise to you, but a lot of the posties would be on something. So often in the morning, guys would walk by me stinking of booze or drugs, sometimes both and these guys were out there driving the roads in your neighborhoods. With myself, it wasn't booze; it was pot; when I was driving the step van delivering parcels, I would go into the back of the truck with my hash pipe and use the ventilation flaps, that were there to let out some of the hot air out of the truck, to exhale. Every day, I had to numb myself down, self-medicate to survive, and deal with being just a mailman.

It was when I was a mailman that I had my car accident. I had multiple injuries, including a punctured lung, a cracked skull, displaced broken arm, ruptured spleen, and my heel was smashed into eighteen pieces. I was in the hospital for eight weeks and dependent on my morphine pump to relieve the pain. When I was sent home and doing rehab, I was prescribed oxycontin. It was 2004 and the opioid crisis was in full swing, Dr's were more than willing to prescribe pain management, but to their credit, I needed it. I learned to walk again and was in constant pain; every time I said I needed more pills; they were more than happy to write the prescription. This fueled my next addiction. Though those pills were required initially, my dependence on them lasted a little too long, and the doctors were prescribing them for too long. I had completed rehab and returned to work at the post office as an inside worker; I was a 'floor man.' And I was still taking the pills. I didn't realize my dependence on them and how dangerous they were until I was back at work. When I returned, fellow workers heard I had an accident, and their first question was, "did they prescribe oxy? Can I buy a couple from you?" Sometimes the guys asking were just doing it jokingly, but most were doing it because they needed it, and one guy, poor Kevin, asked me with tears in his eyes because he was hurting for them so badly. At this time, as the pills dried up and the doctors slowed down prescribing them, I started doing the coke a lot more. When my prescription would run out, and I had to wait to refill it, I would get some blow.

Now, when you are dealing with a cocaine addiction, it brings out other demons; the cocaine spikes your dopamine so much that you are constantly looking to stimulate the pleasure centers in your head. One of my demons is porn/sex addiction. In my younger years, it was party girls and then strippers, then as I got older and started to withdraw from people, it was porn. My lowest point was when I was coming off the oxy/painkillers from my accident and doing blow while at the post office. I had picked up some blow and was driving around some sketchy neighborhood looking for some company, a polite way of saying looking for a hooker. As I was driving and doing blow, I went by what I thought was a woman; as I slowed down and pulled up, I realized it was a guy dressed as a woman; I asked, "where are the women?" As he approached the car, he saw the blow and said, "I can help you out" I was so fucked up I considered it for a couple of seconds, but as he got closer, I sped away, and the blow spilled on my seat. If there had been a cop car nearby, I would have been busted for sure. It was at that time that I knew I needed to quit.

Most people who suffer from an opioid addiction after accidents end up using heroin, not me; I chose cocaine because it's what I had access to; and the fact that I'm scared of needles were the only reasons I decided on cocaine. It cost a fortune, but suffering from PTSD and not thinking straight, I just kept maxing out my credit cards as I didn't believe in the future. My Uncle Johnny, who had taken me in while I was doing my rehab, knew I had a problem and that I needed help. So, I took a week off work and bought two ounces of pot. When I went off the pills, I couldn't sleep for three days, he stayed up with me, and we smoked all that pot until I passed out. I remember almost having tears in my eyes wanting one of those pills, but my uncle refused, and he just rolled more joints. My Uncle Johnny helped me through the most challenging time of my life and saved me from becoming a junkie; I will always be grateful and in his debt.

From that time of the accident when I lost my son, I was high every minute of every day; for fourteen years, I was stoned from when I woke up to when I went to bed. Pot was my priority and took over my life. I had to numb and suppress my mind from thinking about my son. I was diagnosed with PTSD, and my self-medicating just continued, it worsened, and it took over my life. When I smoked, it would stop my mind from racing, it would stop my mind from remembering, and it would stop my mind from thinking about my son, but more importantly, I wouldn't be able to dream. When I smoked pot, I found that I stopped dreaming, or at least I don't remember them. I would just fade out at bedtime, and my head would be so slow and tired from smoking all day long that it just didn't have the energy or the will to remember. I would wake up feeling tired, but I would have no recollection of any dreams or images while in REM sleep, something we all need to survive and thrive in this world.

As a functioning pothead, my day would consist of waking up and smoking a bowl. Eating breakfast, getting ready for work, and smoking a bowl on the way into whatever job I was working at, the post office, the law office, or on a TV/Movie set, I would constantly be stoned. I would be the guy always going out for coffee mid-morning, and I would smoke a bowl. At lunchtime, I would smoke a bowl. That would keep me going until quitting time, and as soon as I was in my car, I would smoke a bowl. Then it would be dinner and pot all night until bed. Every minute of every day, I was constantly stoned. If I was awake, I was baked. Pot was able to get me through my days, but what kind of days was I living? I was numb, my edge and ambition were gone, and I wasn't living my full potential. I relied on what came to me; I didn't have the motivation or a sense of purpose of going after and working for anything. Also, after the car accident, I suffered from what they call 'survivors guilt' and PTSD, which left me feeling I didn't deserve anything, so I didn't work towards anything; I just took what came to me. And as much as I wanted to quit getting high, I just never could.

I could never quit getting buzzed; I always had to abuse one substance or another. The only thing I was ever able to quit was cigarettes. I must have tried to quit a dozen times, trying many different avenues. My first attempts were half-assed attempts, I would try quitting cold turkey, but I would cave into the cravings and start up again after two or three days. I'll never forget one of the first times I tried to quit smoking, I was about two or three days into it, and my body felt like it was going through some changes; I had a strong urge to lie down mid-afternoon to take a nap. The next day, I couldn't get out of bed until three pm; I remember waking up once; I had no idea when it was, but I woke up with chills and shivering and in a pool of sweat. I remember sitting up in bed and watching the sweat dripping off my forehead like it was pouring out; it was a constant stream. I lied back down, went back to sleep, and didn't wake up till the following evening; when I did, I felt like I was coming down from heroin addiction. I got dressed, went to the store, and bought a pack of smokes, and smoked half of it that night.

I had tried to quit smoking with the pills, but they tripped me out; I tried to quit with nicotine chewing gum, but they burned my mouth, and I even tried hypnotism, but nothing worked. It wasn't until I was ultimately sick of smoking and had convinced my mind that I needed to quit. I had made up my mind, but I also needed something to help me with the physical withdrawals of nicotine, so I decided to use the nicotine patch. I had a buddy who wanted to quit simultaneously, so we started on the patch together. It was fantastic; the patches begin at a high dose of nicotine. As you progress, you switch to a lower dosage, and the longer you use them, the more it relieves the physical aspect of trying to quit, but if you have the mental part of quitting made up in your mind, the patches help. We were on the last phase and were supposed to switch down to the weakest patch, and we were both feeling good. Unfortunately, he decided that he had beat it and didn't follow through all the way, skipping the weakest patch. I said, "no way, I'm following through and doing what the instructions tell me to," and I continued to use the lowest patch, he didn't. I was able to quit smoking successfully, and he started smoking again in two weeks!

Addiction is hard. We all need some help when it comes to quitting something. Alcoholics have Alcoholics Anonymous and various drugs to help them stop, opioid users have Narcotics Anonymous and methadone, but the one drug they don't have anything to help you quit is marijuana. They may prescribe anti-depressants as they did with me, but that's not a solution in my mind. You are now just altering your brain chemistry with another drug, albeit a legal one, a doctor prescribed drug, but another drug, nonetheless. When I was addicted to pot, no one in my life thought it was a problem, or at least they didn't say anything; it's not like alcohol or opioids; it's just pot, so no one, including myself, worried about it. So, in my mind, there wasn't anything to help me quit, even though I knew it was stifling me. I didn't know what to do until I learned about 'the mushroom.'

Depression.

Some mornings when I wake up, my head weighs a thousand pounds; it seems so heavy that I can't even lift it off the pillow. It feels like a cinder block that is impossible to move; I just want to bury it deeper into my bed and never move it again. I open my eyes, and it feels as if my mind has been hollowed out of my head, and when I close them, everything seems to feel better. I'll roll over and pull the pillows on top of my head, trying to bury it, just to make things feel right. I know that getting up and moving will be better for me, but it feels so pointless, I will just roll over and go back to sleep. If I had to go to work or had plans for the day, I would just call in sick or cancel anything I had planned. I've lost jobs and friends because it's hard to keep friends when you cancel and piss them off like that. This has happened off and on through every stage of my life; no matter how I tried to numb it, I could never chase it away, and I thought those feelings would never leave me.

I remember being depressed as young as six or seven years old. As a child, my dreams haunted and scared the hell out of me, I would wake up screaming and crying, and when my parents came to calm me, I couldn't tell them what scared me. One such recurring dream I would have that I will never forget involved a group of masked men coming into the neighborhood and going door to door, shooting everyone. I survived because I was hidden under my blankets, and they couldn't find me. Then in the dream I would live my life somewhere else, away from the family I had nothing in common with. My dreams, or should I say my nightmares reflected my feelings of alienation from being raised in an adoptive family that I just never fit in with. So how could I tell them what was scaring me?

I was adopted by older parents and raised with one brother that was four years older than me. He was borderline Asperger Syndrome and would be on the Autism Spectrum by today's standards, but it wasn't as widely known back then. My parents would never acknowledge this and chalked it up that he is just a quiet 'loner', but our household considered him normal. According to them, he was what kids were supposed to be like, and they always told me that I should be more like him. As a result, I was constantly being told that I wasn't normal.

Meanwhile, I loved being around people. I was outgoing, fun-loving, always had lots of friends, and I was very athletic. But, because my parents were a little older, they couldn't handle my energy. I was an active child, always wanting to be moving and energetic, yet my family was a bunch of readers. I remember sitting and crying one night because I had nothing to do, and they told me to sit there and 'be still.'

I just needed stimulation, and when my hyperactivity got too much for them, they just constantly compared me to my brother, and they always said to me, "why can't you be normal like your brother? You're wild; you need to be more like him". They wanted me to be more like the kid with no friends, sitting in the corner alone, playing with dolls.

I started looking for escapes as early as I could, which I think fuels my addictive personality. My first addiction was sugar; I loved candy of any kind. And from what I know about sugar addiction and my later experience with it in life, it's just like cocaine. I know how it affects your brain; it makes you feel good when you are feeling bad. At about ten or eleven years old, I discovered music; I loved The Doors, The Beatles, and when I heard Led Zeppelin on the radio, I loved it. But my parents were older and didn't like rock 'n' roll, and when they listened to some of the songs I was listening to, it scared the hell out of them. When I was caught listening to music, again, I was compared to the quiet kid in the corner reading comic books "why can't you be like your brother?". So, after listening to music, I started to write; I thought I would write some poems or songs. This pleased my parents as it kept me quiet and out of their hair, but when my mom read some of the words, it freaked her out; I don't remember what it was that I wrote. All I remember was that my mom threw out my notebook and asked again, "what's wrong with you? Why can't you be like your brother?" I had a lot of energy as a child, I still do, but as a child, it was hard for my parents to handle. Today it might be called ADHD or hyperactivity, and they didn't know how to handle it, especially when their first child was so quiet, reserved, and introverted.

My experiences with psychiatrists would start at an early age. When I was a kid in grade six, I started stealing. I would take anything that wasn't nailed down. I didn't need the stuff; I was just rebelling, looking for attention and excitement. My parents thought I was the devil's child and didn't know what to do, so my mom decided to take me to a child psychiatrist. On the way to the appointment, my mom told me that we were going to see our family doctor, Dr. Jones. When I saw my report cards in the car, I asked, "why are my report cards here?". My mom said that Dr. Jones wanted to see them. Now, I may have been a kid, but I wasn't stupid, I called her out on it; and she lied the entire way there, I knew something was up and felt so alienated again. I remember this was when the relationship with my mom was never the same.

The psychiatrist was an old guy who must have been about sixty years old and made appointments out of his house. How my parents thought this guy was going to relate to me, I would never understand. The only thing we did for the couple of appointments that I went to was play chess, which did nothing for me. He asked, "do you know how to play chess?" I said, "no," and he replied, "oh, that's too bad; a lot of kids your age know how to play." Great, thanks for making me feel inadequate once again; every way I turned as a kid, I had adults telling me I wasn't the norm.

My teenage years were challenging and filled with constant fighting at home. I didn't do too well at school because it bored the hell out of me, so I wasn't there much. I started skipping school and rebelling, hanging out with the wrong crowd, and when I was sixteen, I dropped out of school and ran away from home. I couch-surfed with friends when I could, and when there was nowhere to sleep, I just slept outside in parks in the neighborhood; they call it 'on the streets' or 'homeless.' Not having a home was hard to handle, but at least I wasn't arguing and fighting with anyone anymore. After a year of not doing too good on my own, I went back home, but nothing changed. The arguing, the fighting, and the alienation began immediately, so smoking pot and alcohol would be my only escape.

After about six months of being back home, I had one of the darkest moments of my life. I was out with friends who had a band; we were at a recording studio because they were laying down some tracks for a demo album. I had just turned seventeen and was the youngest kid there. It was close to my curfew, so I called home to explain where I was and wouldn't be home until later. My mom freaked out, starting yelling, and screaming for me to come home even though I explained where I was, what we were doing, and how I thought it was amazing and one of the coolest things I had ever done and that I really wanted to stay. All she could do was tell me how rotten and terrible I was and that if I didn't come home, I would be thrown out. I remember the guys making jokes as I told them I had to leave. I hated that she made me leave, so before I left, I bought a bottle of vodka from one of the guys. I proceeded to get shit faced before I got home; the funny thing was, I hadn't been drinking or smoking anything that night since I was having so much fun in the recording studio. I was dreading going home, and when I got there, I knew why; my mom was borderline psychotic. All she could do was scream, "what an animal I was, I never would be anything, and why couldn't I be more like my brother" normal like him, the guy that had no friends and just sat in the corner reading comic books. I couldn't take it anymore; I went upstairs and took every pill in the medicine cabinet. It mainly was Tylenol, Aspirin, and a couple of prescriptions of which I had no idea what they were. I tried to kill myself because I just couldn't take it anymore, but luckily, I didn't. I cried myself to sleep, hoping I wasn't going to wake up. But, I had so much poison in my system from the booze, cigarettes, and pills that I just puked, pissed, and shit everything out as I slept.

Not my best moment, but thankfully I didn't choke or suffocate on my vomit. I woke up at two in the afternoon to yelling and screaming. I remember crying that I was still there but happy that I was still alive. Now, I admit that there would have been worst homes and environments to grow up in, I was never beaten or physically abused, and my parents were always able to provide for me. Still, my dad was an absentee father, and my mom was an "OCD" control freak who thought the kid with the Asperger's was the norm. My parents always told me that I wasn't any good; I wasn't a normal person and constantly compared to my brother, who I knew, wasn't the norm. That takes a toll on a young, sensitive, fragile child, and I couldn't take it.

As a teenager, I would start withdrawing from my interests and friends, and that trend would continue into my adulthood. In high school, I stopped playing team sports, drifted from friends I knew for years, and started hanging out with other troubled youth. I stopped talking to any of the friends I grew up with and started hanging out with the punks, skinheads, and rockers, all the kids that were trying to rebel in any way they could. I didn't fit in with any of these groups; I was just a kid who liked partying and was a 'misfit.' My friends had long hair, shaved heads, mohawks, colored hair, and tattoos, all before it was cool to have any of these things. In my day, if you looked like that, you were considered a 'freak,' a 'weirdo,' or a 'punk.' The people I knew wore leather, ripped jeans, had marker drawings of bands and symbols on their clothes. Everyone was different, we were all unique, and we were all looked down upon by teachers, parents, and anyone of authority. We were different, but we all had something in common; none of us felt we fit in anywhere, and we all liked getting fucked up; drinking and drugs are what we all had in common.

I was never happy where I was in life. I graduated high school a year later than all my friends; I watched them go off to university while I was still in high school, and I had no clue what I would do when I graduated. Not knowing my future left me with such a feeling of inadequacy. It made me feel as if I wasn't as good as everyone else, everyone I knew, and of course, my brother went to university. Again, I wasn't an ordinary person or as good as my brother in my parents' eyes. This feeling of inadequacy would never leave me, even as I succeeded. When I started excelling in my retail career, I still felt inadequate; retail was looked down upon and not a 'good' career in my parents' eyes. Even though I was starting to get into management, it wasn't your traditional nine-to-five shirt-and-tie job.

When I was twenty-three, I was working my ass off in retail when my son was born. His mother and I only dated for six months when she got pregnant, she was a hot party girl, and that's all I was looking for at the time. When she called to tell me that she was pregnant, I hoped that she was calling to break up with me. But instead, she said the words, "I'm pregnant." I couldn't believe it, my whole life flashed in front of my eyes, everything I thought I was going to be and do in life seemed to escape from my mind, I couldn't believe it. Being adopted, all I wanted in this world was to have a family and to be a good Father, but this wasn't going to happen. The saying is true, those that forget their past are destined to repeat it, well I was adopted born out of a loveless fling, and here I am repeating it. We broke up before he was born, but I vowed that I would always be there for him, and I was, but she wanted none of that; she just wanted the support paycheck that went along with having a baby. When my child was born, she went into hiding, she took off, and I had to track her down and find her. We were in family court from the day he was born. I had to fight for the right to see my son, and we were in family court his entire life. The most beautiful gift in the world, a beautiful, a fantastic child who was supposed to make me feel good and proud, only made me feel depressed and unworthy. Something that was supposed to bring such joy brought pain and suffering because of his mom; this changed me as a man; it broke me.

I started taking anti-depressants around the age of twenty-four. I was working in management in retail; it was more tedious than nine to five, I was working sixty to seventy hours a week, and my sons' mom was making my life a living hell. She kept coming after me for more money and more stipulations of my access to him. It was a time that 'deadbeat dads' were all over the news, and she was able to use the full powers of the family court system against me. If you were an honest man trying to do the right thing and caught up in that system during that time, you were screwed, and they really screwed me. The laws were written in favor of women, rightfully so, there were many men not living up to their responsibility, but I was not one of them. All I wanted to be, was a father to my son, but the mom wouldn't let me; all she wanted from me was my paycheck. Being crushed by the court system and working my ass off took its toll. I went to the doctor, and he prescribed me Effexor; this would be the beginning of taking antidepressants on and off throughout my entire life.

I wasn't excited about taking anti-depressants; it seemed like a crutch, just another drug to get me by. I took them for a couple of years, and they seemed just to let me accept the things I didn't like in my life. I wasn't happier; I was just more accepting of the things in my life that made me miserable. I was still smoking a ton of pot when I was taking the anti-depressants, and I was drinking whenever I wanted to. All the anti-depressants seemed to do was make me accept things in my life that I didn't like; I still had to alter my mind and consciousness. I needed to escape. After a couple of years, I got used to life. I was in a good place and thought I didn't need the pills anymore, so I stopped taking them. A year went by, and everything was fine. I was working my ass off and juggling my schedule to see my son; it was hectic and a lot of work, and I was almost happy in life. But then the mom came back at me for more money with the full support of the family court system, they came at me again and beat me down. Her lawyers were paid for by the welfare system, while I had to drain my bank account just to be a part of my sons' life. I was draining my bank account to be a father to my son, it was putting me into bankruptcy. I was going broke paying lawyers, but the courts didn't care; they were more than happy to entertain the mom's vindictive and unreasonable behavior. Her lawyers, the judge, the court employees were all getting paid while

I was going bankrupt; it made me realize what our system is all about. It didn't matter that I was working sixty to seventy hours a week for a better future; it didn't matter that I was working my ass off and trying to be a part of my son's life; their only priority was money, how much do I make and how much should I pay. The court system didn't care about the games the mom was playing or about the psychological damage she was doing to me and the child. It was all about money. It was like the line out of 'Goodfellas' the movie, "working your ass off every day, 'fuck you pay me'; working sixty to seventy hours a week; 'fuck you, pay me'; struggling to get by, 'fuck, you pay me'; the mom is psychologically abusing you and your son, 'fuck you, pay me'". This struck me to my core, and I went back into a depression, so to make it through, I went back on the anti-depressants, and it seemed to make everything in my life ok, but it wasn't, they just took the fight out of me and made me accept the shit that was my life.

Medicating for depression was a constant battle; take the anti-depressants and just accept what was going on in my life. They didn't give me ambition. They didn't make me happier; they just made me acceptant of the bullshit that I should usually not accept. They just made me say, "it is what it is," which I feel is a horrible saying. To me, it means that you are not willing to change the situation at hand; you are just acceptant and unwilling to try to make a change. Whoever coined the phrase 'it is, what it is' was a defeatist that must have been on anti-depressants. The anti-depressants made me crave sugar like a coke addict, and I couldn't get enough of the stuff. They also affected my sex life, I wasn't dating regularly, but when I would meet someone and was at the point of getting intimate, the dam thing wouldn't work; I wasn't able to get aroused. I went to the doctor, and he prescribed Viagra; now I needed another pill just to have sex; this didn't seem right to me, so I stopped taking the 'happy pills,' and I started to live my life without them again.

Everything was good for about a year. Life was mellowing out, work was tolerable, and the relationship with my son was getting stronger; I was starting to enjoy life a little a bit. But then, once again, the mom and court came back at me for more money; I was pissed off, demoralized, and crushed. All I wanted to be, was a good Father and all the mom wanted was more money. Finally, I had had enough; the system beat me down and broke me; I decided that if all they wanted was money, I wouldn't have any. If I didn't have a job, they couldn't come after me for more money. So, I quit my job, kept paying the original support payment amount (I always honored my obligations, I was not, and never was a 'deadbeat dad'), and lived off my savings for a year. I moved in with my brother, I lived on his couch and smoked pot every minute of the day, the only time I was straight was when I had my son every other weekend; it was the only time I was happy and didn't need to numb myself.

After a year of doing nothing and living in despair and darkness, I went back to the doctor to seek help. This time he prescribed the anti-depressant Cipralex. Under this false sense of well-being, I took a job at the Post Office. Now, no one wants to work at the post office, I felt like I sacrificed trying to be anything of worth in this world to be a mailman, but it was worth it for my son. Being a mailman allowed me the time and energy to be with him on the weekends; I would finish early on Fridays, so I could pick him up and have no pressure from work. Once I finished my route, I was done, nothing to think about and no work to take home with me at night or on the weekends. The anti-depressants seemed to let me accept everything wrong in my life, and even though I accepted working at the post office, deep down, I didn't like what I became; I just felt I could do more with my life. Pot smoking, drinking, hard drugs, and binge eating became my life as a mailman. Walking up and down the same streets, day after day, really takes a toll on your mind. People would say to me, "being a letter carrier is a great job", "yeah, have you ever done it?" would be my reply. It hit home one day as I was walking the route, and a woman asked me, "don't you get bored walking up and down the same streets day after day?" My reply, "Lady, I'm so stoned I hardly know where I am!" She looked at me shocked, then laughed, she thought I was joking; then I laughed because I knew I was dead serious.

It was at this time when I had my car accident. I was walking the route and getting my son every second weekend, and I was acceptant of my life when it happened. It was a two-vehicle collision on a one-way highway early in the morning when I was taking him back. My son died on that road, and I was airlifted out, I was near death, but that was nothing compared to what I lost. My beautiful eight-year-old son died one week before his ninth birthday. People think they know what depression is; they feel that their day-to-day problems are depression; imagine having the most beautiful thing in front of you, losing it, and wishing you were dead daily. Every day wishing you could look at them or reach out and touch them, or just even hear their voice. After he died, it was like losing a limb, you think it is still there, and it isn't. It was in the court order that I would get to call him once a week and speak to him on the phone; years after the accident, I would wake up and think that it was time to call him, then the realization would hit me again that I would never get the chance to speak to him again. I thought I was depressed before the accident; I would never know depression and chemical dependence like I would in the next fifteen years of my life.

After the accident, I had to go to therapy. I never knew a person could cry so deep and so hard. I hurt deep down past my heart, and all my brain could think about was my son. I went to grief counseling during my rehabilitation which was a big help; it was the first time in my life that I felt therapy finally helped. Unfortunately, it was paid for by the insurance company and only lasted for a little while. When it ran out, it was on to a psychiatrist who once again prescribed anti-depressants. This time it was Effexor. This guy was useless except for the prescription pad he had; I resented talking to him. After a while, I quit seeing him and went to the family doctor to get my Effexor prescription. When my physical rehab finished, I returned to work at the post office, but I couldn't walk the route anymore, so I returned as the night 'floor man'. That job was depressing as hell; the only good thing was that I could smoke as much pot as I wanted to, as there was hardly anyone around. The night supervisor was usually drunk, and he always snuck out to sleep in his car for hours.

I was depressed as hell, living with the memory of my son, and working in a dead-end job, I couldn't see the future, and I had no idea where my life was going. The more depressed I got, the more Effexor they prescribed me and the more acceptable I became of everything wrong in my life. I had no clue what I would do with my life, so I became a supervisor. A supervisor at the Post Office is probably the worst job I have ever had. The workers hate you, and upper management has no respect for you. They make you do the dirty work of enforcing their policies and demoralizing the workers. Most supervisors were drunks with broken marriages, and life wasn't kind to them. My boss was even missing some teeth, missing teeth, and we had a great dental plan! The people there are so depressed and lacking self-esteem that they couldn't even be bothered to get their teeth fixed. I didn't want to end up like them, so I had to get the hell out of there. I was looking for options when an opportunity came along. My old boss from the retail company moved to Jamaica and got the franchise rights to open the Hard Rock Café in Ocho Rios, Jamaica. She asked me what I was doing and asked if I wanted to come down and open the retail section of the restaurant. Of course, I jumped at the opportunity; I looked forward to leaving everything behind and was looking forward to living and working in a new place. I took a leave of absence from the post office and went down. For the first time in a long-time, I looked forward to the future, and finally, I had optimism for what was ahead of me.

Though Jamaica was beautiful, it wasn't a good fit for me; little did I know, but my boss was a functioning cocaine addict, a daily user that made her a crazy lady from hell. She wasn't too bad when she was using, but she was a crazy irrational nightmare when she wasn't. She would make the staff, who gave her the name 'dragon lady,' cry every day and treated them like slaves. She ran all her employees into the ground, including me. Aside from that nightmare, being a white guy living in Jamaica can be very alienating; the murder rate is unbelievable and kidnappings of foreign (white) businesspeople, was an industry down there. I wasn't allowed to go out without Ricky, my black escort. I could only walk from my apartment building, 'The Turtle Towers', where the cruise ships came to dock, to the café, a heavy tourist area, which meant it had a large police presence. When I first got there, the locals would swarm me trying to sell me weed, parasailing deals, and anything else they were trying to hustle. It took a couple of weeks for them to accept me as a local and they would just say here come the 'Yardi boy' when they saw me coming; it was at this point that I felt accepted.

Being alone down there was hard and very lonely, so drinking, smoking pot, doing blow, and partying kept me company. My low self-esteem and PTSD led me to make some bad decisions, which almost got me killed or thrown into a Jamaican prison. I would spend my nights at Margaritaville; it was located just across the street from my apartment at the 'Turtle Towers,' so it was just a stumble distance home. I would drink and party with people from all over the world; one night, I was partying with Dave from Vancouver. Dave wanted some blow and was bugging me all night to do some; after a while, I caved, and we went into the bathroom and a stall. I should have known better, I was drunk, depressed and I let my guard down. When we came out of the stall, an undercover cop was standing there, and Dave still had the little baggy in his hand.

The cop saw it and immediately radioed to the uniform officers that were waiting outside the bar. He patted Dave down and told him to stand against the wall. He then proceeded to pat me down; as he did, I asked him, 'Is it going to be the left or the right?' He looked at me and told me to stand behind him; I went and stood behind him and drank from the beer that I was still holding.

When the uniforms came in, he instructed them to take Dave away for cocaine possession. I'll never forget the look of fear and confusion in Dave's eyes as he was led away. He just stared at me as he was handcuffed and escorted out by the Jamaican Police. I knew what he was thinking; he was wondering why wasn't I going to jail with him? You see, when I got to Jamaica, my boss was partnered with a very 'connected' businessman down there. My boss had told me that the cops are tolerant of marijuana smoking, but cocaine was a big 'no-no,' and would never be overlooked; she said to me that if I was ever caught doing anything, ask the cop, 'is it going to be the left or the right?' Having no idea what that meant, I had to ask her what she meant. She explained that the cops are so poor and so corrupt that you can almost always bribe your way out of anything, but you can't be so blatant just to ask, 'how much to let me go?' Cause if anyone heard you, then you are in shit for trying to bribe a cop, and the cop would be in trouble too. But if you ask, 'is it the left or the right?' no one knows what you are talking about (like Dave, for example) except for the crooked cops. What it means to the cop is, 'Is this going to be for the right hand for writing me a ticket, or the left hand for your lunch money?'. I'm so glad I had the guts to ask, and as soon as he separated Dave and me, I knew this guy wanted to be paid. When he walked me outside, he asked, "how much do you have" "I said I had one thousand Jamaican," which was about one hundred U.S; it was enough to keep me out of jail. I'll never forget that night, and I'll never forget poor

Dave; I always wondered whatever happened to Dave from Vancouver.

Being a white guy working in Jamaica, everyone thinks you're rich, which was very far from the truth; I was just a working guy like everyone else down there, but they couldn't see that. It was very alienating and lonely. The girls want to be with you just to get their hooks into you to have a baby and help them get the hell out of there, and the guys want to be your friends just because they think you have money. Just when you think someone is being your friend and wants to get to know you, it eventually leads to, "Hey, can you give me some money?". After a while, the loneliness got to me, and I turned to cocaine. The cocaine was phenomenal down there, and it was very cheap, but more importantly, it made the loneliness disappear. It helped me get through my depression and sadness, but then it got a hold of me; I was turning into my boss, and it started to control me. I started partying way too much and exercising some self-destructive behavior.

Another poor decision I made was staying out and partying too late one night. I was always told to get home by ten or eleven, and one night I stayed at Margaritaville until about three or four in the morning. When I stumbled out of there and started walking home, there was a group of young Jamaicans hanging out in the road between Margaritaville and my apartment. I was hammered and didn't care, I kept going and when they approached me, I knew I was in trouble as they were angry. They started saying things like, "whitey comes down and takes our jobs, comes down and takes what's ours." They started shoving and pushing me around, and when I heard them say things like, "let's stab him, no let's take him, someone will pay, let's make some money," I was at a low point, and I guess you could say I was at rock bottom, and when they said, "let's make some money", it triggered me. I started screaming and crying, "I had enough of this world, everyone wants money, I got nothing in this world, I got no money, I don't have things, I don't want anything in this world except to see my son again." This took them by surprise, and they stopped. I was crying and yelling, "God took my firstborn son, God took him away from me and I don't care about anything, you want to kill me, kill me, you'd be doing me a favor, you want to be man, kill me and be a man, I don't give a fuck come on let's go, what are you waiting for." This took them by even more surprise. I didn't know what would happen when the situation escalated to them pushing, shoving, and talking of murdering or kidnapping me, and I certainly didn't see it ending this way. They took pity on me. I guess mentioning God and hearing how young my son was when he died made them think and feel bad for me.

I sat on the ground and kept crying; they sat down with me, started consoling me, and asking me questions. We started talking, and they began rolling joints; I pulled out my pot and told them to spin it up. It seemed I touched a nerve with them. They all had friends and family that were killed way too young due to gang violence and senseless murders due to the poverty of Jamaica. At this point, I knew I wasn't recovered and still suffering from grief and PTSD. I knew that if I stayed in Jamaica, I would die from drugs, alcohol, or who knows what else. This was when I decided I needed to leave.

I could only stay in Jamaica in Jamaica for six months. I was supposed to be there for a year. It was too much, my boss, the coke, the loneliness, and the alienation. So, I left, and after almost getting killed and thrown in jail, I skipped out of there. I remember the night I left; I asked the cabbie to get some coke before going to the airport. He made a couple of stops and was able to grab me a gram; I got a hotel room to do it all before I got on the plane. I was so depressed that I didn't give a shit if I was all messed up when I flew out there; I just had to get the hell out of there and back to Toronto. When I flew back, I was in such a hurry I didn't check my luggage thoroughly enough; I had accidentally brought back a couple of grams of weed in the outer sleeve of my suitcase that wasn't even zipped up. Surprisingly and luckily, I made it through customs with no problem!

When I got back to Toronto, I went right back to work at the Post Office, back into the life I hated and the life I was trying to run away from. I didn't think my depression couldn't get any worse, but it did. Life settled into the boring 'going nowhere' routine, and there were reminders of my son Dalton everywhere I went. Smoking a truckload of pot daily helped me forget and helped me keep my PTSD 'at bay'. As many flaws as Jamaica had, it was a beautiful country with beautiful nature. The ocean, the beaches, fern gulley, and the foliage put me at peace somewhat, and returning to the factory life of the post office was depressing as hell. So again, I started looking for a way to get out of the post office.

After about a year, the opportunity came again. A friend, or at least what I thought was a friend, was in the business of debt collections. He and a colleague decided to venture out on their own and do debt collections in a law office, all they needed was a lawyer and a sales department, and that's where I came in; I would be the sales department. They promised a job for life if I helped them build up the business, and since he was a friend, or so I thought, I thought I could trust him, and I jumped at the chance. I knew nothing about sales, but I was damn good at it. It was tough initially, and I was on anti-depressants when I started, but I made it work, and after three years, we were rocking. I had the knack, and people liked me, so making connections was easy. I was able to land some Fortune Five Hundred clients and built the business up for them. I settled into the routine, and I started liking life, and I was enjoying it. I hadn't been to a psychiatrist for a while, and my PTSD seemed to be in check. I was still smoking pot constantly and drinking whenever and even using cocaine occasionally since I was making such good money.

As we started to make money, things changed, my boss never had money before, but his partner came from it, so he wasn't the problem, but when my boss got a taste of money, it changed him. It's true what they say, 'money changes people'. He wanted more for himself and was jealous of me, even though I worked for him. When I signed a big company, all the employees would congratulate me and just ignore him; after all, he was just the asshole bill collector; I was the one they liked. Finally, he couldn't stand it and wanted more money, so he fired me. They used the excuse that I was underperforming, and instead of putting up a fight, I left. In hindsight, I should have sued their asses off. But that wasn't me, I didn't want them in my life anymore or the strife, so I took the piddly severance and left. In hindsight, it was a mistake, but I was better off not having to deal with those two assholes anymore. I still know people connected to them, so I hear about them occasionally. I hear how they never really recovered from losing me and are always trying to hire new sales staff. People go to work for them and leave in a short while because no one wants to work for assholes like those two guys.

It seems that my mental health has always been connected to my employment. I always did just enough to get by, an 'over-achieving under-achiever', nothing excited me enough to want to excel. Even women in my adult years never made me want to achieve great things like they did when I was young. After the experiences with my son's mother, I was deeply scarred, and it left me with the feeling that whatever I would accomplish could be taken away from me. I mean, at the time, I was a hard-working, energetic young man who was working his ass off and just trying to make right by his son. But his mom and the family court system didn't care about any of that. Even when I excelled in the Law Office, I learned that whatever you accomplish can be taken away from you unless you are doing something absolutely for yourself. After leaving the Law Office, I went into a deep funk, and I knew if I didn't do something, I could easily absorb into my couch for months feeling hopeless and lost. I decided to pack the car and go for a drive. I drove for three days and ended up on the East Coast in Nova Scotia. I grabbed a cheap motel and decided to check out the ocean and do some thinking.

After some reflection, I figured out what I was going to do. I was tired of working for someone else when it could all be taken away from me at their whim. I was tired of making other people rich. I asked myself, 'what have I always wanted to do and what would be just for me?' I decided to throw caution to the wind and go into acting. I had some severance pay, so I decided to give it a shot. I got in the car and headed back to Toronto; I enrolled in some acting classes and started hustling. I was happy with my choice, but for someone that is borderline manic-depressive and suffering from PTSD, acting is a hard gig to handle. The rejections, the ups, the downs of the industry are hard to handle, but I started to have fun in my life. No longer was I responsible for others or accountable to bosses and superiors. I was doing something just for me, responsible for no one except myself. I had little responsibility, and I didn't give a shit what anyone thought of that. I didn't have the 'prestige' of working in a Law Office, I wasn't controlling meetings in the board room, nor did I have the respect of an entire workforce like at the post office, and I certainly wasn't making the money I used to, but I was happy.

Even though I was happier and having fun, one thing remained, I was constantly stoned and drinking like a fish. I was working on TV/Movie sets big and small in Toronto, which is considered 'Hollywood North,' and I was partying more than I ever had; I was now in a business conducive to alcoholism and substance abuse. The first day I worked as an extra on set, it was on the show 'Suits,' the guy I sat beside looked at me and said, "how much cocaine did you bring?" As you can guess, we became good friends.

But after a few years, the depression persisted, I would think of my son constantly, and the only way to numb and suppress those thoughts was to smoke a truckload of pot. I was stoned continuously from morning to night. I would wake and bake in the morning, hits from the bong and the pipe all day long, and a joint before bed to help me sleep. It was the only way I knew how to deal with the guilt, regret, and sadness that filled me. The TV/Movie business was constant ups and downs, work for a week, don't work for two, work for two weeks, don't work for a month, there's a lot of downtimes and a lot of time to think. If you don't keep your mind busy and occupied, you can go to some dark places.

It got to the point that I couldn't continue the way I was living. I was still depressed as hell, and I was tired of numbing myself; it wasn't working anymore. I've heard of people living happy lives, but I never understood how and why. So, I figured it was time for a change. It was time for a change on my terms. And my terms were going to be using psychedelics to end my addiction and depression once and for all.

Ways I Have Tried to Quit.

Over the course of thirty-five years, I have tried many ways to deal with my depression and addictions. I have tried the usual doctor-recommended paths, cold turkey, and a couple of my crazy ideas. Every few years, I would get conscious of where my life was at, I was never happy with myself, and I always thought it was time for a change. So off I would go and start the 'recovery' process again and try to quit everything that I thought was making me unhappy.

I would do whatever the doctors would recommend. When I followed the traditional 'medically supervised' recovery steps, every attempt to quit would start with a trip to the family doctor, who would refer me to whatever treatment he thought was appropriate for me at the time. It was kind of like the 'white coat lottery.' I knew I was there to get treatment, but I never really knew what would be recommended. Over the years, it would be psychotherapists, rehab, Narcotics Anonymous, Alcoholics Anonymous, and psychiatrists; oh, there would be lots of psychiatrists! I have also tried 'non-traditional' or 'not doctor-recommended avenues to quit. These included hypnotism, sensory deprivation, cold turkey, oh, there would be many cold turkeys, and what I call 'the substitution method,' trying to replace one substance for another.

My first attempt to quit was when I was twenty-one. I was working a shitty job landscaping; it was fun, hard work in the fresh air, but it was a 'nowhere' job; it just put beer money in my pocket. Already a chronic pothead and heavy binge drinker, I was smoking every day, and on weekends I was binge drinking until I would blackout; a case of beer and a 'mickey' of vodka was the norm. The problem was that my weekends turned into long weekends, then the long weekends turned into a week, and my week that was supposed to be clean and sober got smaller and smaller and was eventually swallowed by my weekends; there wasn't a day of sobriety. So, my first 'kick at the can' at sobriety was a full-time rehab program when I was twenty-one years old, it was twenty-one days, so I took that as a sign that it would work (so naïve).

Having health insurance is a hell of a thing. I have tried to get mental health support when covered and when not covered by insurance and let me tell you, there is a hell of a difference in what you receive with and without coverage. The first attempt I made to quit was covered by insurance. The start of the 'white coat rehab process' begins with a trip to the family doctor where you have to admit to him that you are suffering, hurting, and need help, so that you can get that referral note to make sure the insurance company will pay for it. That in itself is a sobering conversation and does kind of help. They say the first step in recovery is admitting you have a problem, and when you hear yourself describing it to someone, it is a little bit of a wake-up call.

Growing up, I suffered from depression, and I was never happy. I had a good upbringing, my parents were good providers in the material category, but they left something to be desired in the mental realm. We all went to the same family doctor. So, when I went to him, he was very concerned because no one else in my family was a drinker or substance abuser (my birth family is a different story), so he thought my behavior was very out of the norm. He recommended the extreme, a full-time twenty-one-day rehab program, it wasn't a live-in rehabilitation, but it was pretty damn intense. It was a little unheard of to quit your job or schooling to go into a full-time rehab program for three weeks. But that is what you get when you have a doctor who cares for you and when you have health insurance. I guess he thought I would be able to quit with such a radical step, but it wouldn't be for a few years until we both realized how 'hell-bent' I was on altering my mind and how dependent I would be with pot, with alcohol and escaping reality. I'm not going to go into great detail about every time I've tried to quit; I'm just going to give you the ways I have tried to quit.

So off I went to rehab; I quit my shitty landscaping job, which I hated anyway, and went to learn about why I liked to get messed up all the time. Rehab was an experience and a half. I'll never forget where the doctor sent me, 'The Donwoods Institute,' and it was right in my neighborhood. It was a few acres that were tucked in a little valley behind our neighborhood and looked like a summer retreat for the rich. I felt like I was on vacation when I walked in. People were sitting by trees reading in the shade, a few guys were throwing a frisbee, and it looked as if a bunch of campers were seated in a circle listening to someone giving a lecture. Where the hell was I? When I got there for the orientation, I noticed I was the youngest in the group; everyone else was over forty years except for one gentleman, we'll call him Steve, and we were all male. After orientation, we could go get something to eat; we could snack and drink anytime we wanted; if you felt a little hungry, that's ok, go on over to the dining hall and get something to eat; there was even a Sundae bar! It turns out having a drinking and drug problem can be kind of fun.

I bonded with Steve; he was a little younger than the others, probably in his late thirties, and worked in sales. He said he liked to drink before he landed his job, but it was his job that turned him into an alcoholic. Part of the job in sales was taking clients out, entertaining them, and closing the deal, so he was always drinking at lunches and dinners. He said his drinking wasn't a problem as long as the clients were coming in, but once sales slowed down, so did his bosses' patience with his drinking; he was given the ultimatum, stop drinking or stop working there. So, Steve was there just to appease his bosses. A week into the program, I remember walking past one of the local neighborhood bars, and I saw Steve out on the patio having a pitcher of beer. I didn't let him see me, and the next day I asked him what he got up to last night, he replied, "not much." He completed the program but might have been drunk while accepting his 'clean and sober' certificate. I always wondered what happened to that guy.

The rest of the people in my 'group' were middle-aged men. Some had lost jobs or wives due to drinking; a couple of guys were having physical problems from drinking, no matter what reason they were there, they all wanted to quit drinking. Most of them looked at me and wondered why I was there; after listening to some of my stories, they figured out I liked to get fucked up. I explained that it was all I thought about, and I knew that if I didn't get a hold of it, it would get a hold of my life, and in hindsight, it did. One guy was particularly judgemental towards me; he was a dick, literally. His name was Richard, who said he was a teacher (no surprise, he was a dick). When he introduced himself to the group, he claimed that it was his job that turned him into an alcoholic. Right away, Steve asked, "what was it, the summers off and all those holidays that made you drink?" That was when I knew I would like Steve. Richard was constantly belittling my addictions and my reason for being in the program. Richard had no sense of humor and a quick fuse. He went into a rant about how evil and disrespectful his students were, but I knew his type; he looked down on the kids with no respect, and I'm sure his students could sense that, so I'm guessing they made his life a living hell, and rightfully so, he was the exact reason I didn't like teachers. When we were in a group session that dealt with past traumas, the counselor mentioned that people are capable of burying and repressing traumatic events that may have happened as children; right away, Richard thought he was abused as a child. It turned out he wasn't. You could suggest anything to this guy, and he thought it applied to him. One day the counselor discussed that repressing homosexuality could cause severe substance abuse in life; when he said this, guess who thought they might be homosexual? Of course, Richard, and of course he wasn't. What a dick.

It would have been a good program if I was a more mature person at that time, it might have worked if there were more people in my demographic, but the program didn't work for me. The days were spent going from one group therapy meeting to another dealing with different emotional issues. There were also activities in between to get you active and in better shape, we got to play badminton, horseshoes, and I learned what 'corn holing' was. At the end of the program, we even got to play a game of baseball against another group. I think you can tell what I took away from the program. If I was a different person or a little older, the program might have worked. The therapies were set up to find past traumas and issues of why you liked to abuse substances. I wouldn't suffer my trauma until later in life when I had my car accident and lost my son; at this point, I was young and still looking for fun, so I didn't think I was anything like the guys in my group, I thought I just liked to party. I stayed clean for a couple of weeks after the rehab, but since I thought the binge drinking was the problem, I kept smoking pot after that, not as much, but still smoking, so I thought cutting down was a victory.

It might have been considered a success because right after I was able to land a job that I would excel at and that would become my career for the next six years. But as the job became a high-pressure job, the more I got promoted, the more I would drink, the more I would smoke pot, and the more caffeine and nicotine I would consume. A little while after landing the job, I had a quick six-month relationship with a party girl; in hindsight, there was nothing 'quick' about it because she got pregnant. When my son Dalton was born, she made my life a living hell; we were in court more than we were together, she tried to take me for all the money I was making, and she took every ounce of my energy. The stress of working sixty to seventy hours a week and working on the road took its toll, couple that with the stress and pressure of family court, I kept smoking pot and drinking like a fiend; it was the only way I could survive and cope. I wouldn't try quitting for another four years.

I was working for a party supply store chain, I was traveling to new markets and opening new retail locations, so I wasn't in the same place for more than a month. I was stressed out; I was drinking and smoking every day, so I decided to get sober using 'AA', Alcoholics Anonymous; that would be my next 'kick at the can.' I was very hesitant about 'AA', but I was desperate, I was constantly stoned, drunk, and it was beginning to take its toll. I heard many mixed messages about AA and that it was almost 'cult' like; it seemed to work for some but not for others, and I heard that you either love it or hate it. So, before I began, I was very hesitant. It was built around meetings and group therapies which I wasn't a big fan of. I chose 'AA' because I was working on the road and could find a meeting in any town, any time. I was hesitant of 'AA' because of its religious affiliations and the rooting in the higher belief of God. They claimed it didn't matter which one you prayed to; they said they love everyone equally, but it seemed they loved you a little more if you prayed to God.

I wasn't optimistic about 'AA'; they have a helpline you can call when you are struggling. I called it and had a talk with a 'recovery/addiction expert' on the phone. It seemed like an initial intake appointment; at the time, I thought it was a good conversation. We talked about how much I was drinking and how much pot I was smoking, how it affected my work, my family, and it seemed like that she genuinely cared. I really thought she was trying to figure out if 'AA' was a good fit for me. She said she was going to send me some pamphlets and information through the mail. When I asked her about 'God' and the connection with 'AA,' she played it down and said, "no, they don't focus on the religious aspect of it." When I got the information and read the '12 Steps' for the first time, I chuckled to myself because 'God' is mentioned in steps number three, five, six, seven, and eleven! 'God' is mentioned in five of the twelve steps, and she claimed 'AA' wasn't affiliated with 'God.' Christ, it was like reading pamphlets from the Catholic Church. If that didn't upset me enough, what bothered me more was the follow-up 'sales calls' they hounded me with before I decided to give them a try. It was lousy telemarketing sales tactics. They called back every other day for about two weeks. After so many calls, I started to push back a little and asked them why so many follow-up sales calls? I got the standard 'script answers' in return, and that's when I learned that I was just talking to some girl in a call center making her calls for her 'client of the day' and that she was just making her quota. It seemed just like any other charity or 'cause', they make their money from donations, and if this group can get their hooks into you while they are brainwashing you away from alcohol, they probably make a good living from the guise of helping people.

Now don't get me wrong, I'm sure 'AA' has helped a lot of people, and if it is a treatment plan that works for you, fantastic, but it didn't for me. I went to a couple of meetings, but the idea of getting up in front of strangers didn't work for me (even though I do it for a living). I disagree with their philosophy of looking to a higher power for guidance; I believe in looking within. When Bill Wilson, founder of 'AA" was able to quit drinking because of LSD therapy, he thought that LSD would help participants reach a spiritual reckoning. He wanted to introduce LSD therapy to the program, but the other founder wouldn't allow it. Bill stated, *"I am certain that the LSD experiment has helped me very much… I find myself with heightened color perception and an appreciation of beauty almost destroyed by my years of depression".* [2] This is well before Timothy Leary and the "turn on, tune in, drop out" movement of the sixties and before Nixon's war on drugs in the seventies (more on that in chapter five). Their idea of helping people quit drinking and struggling with addiction was rooted in the belief that people needed a 'spiritual awakening' to enlighten them about their addictions. Bill Wilson knew that there was no quicker way to a spiritual awakening than psychedelics. But because of their 'connection' to God and the perception that LSD was an evil drug and that it created a "false awakening," it was decided that LSD shouldn't be used in the program. I believe the excuse for not using LSD is due to religious beliefs to an extent, but I also feel 'AA' may have had the same business philosophy as the pharmaceutical industry. How would 'AA' make money if alcoholism can be treated with one, two, or just a few LSD therapy sessions? There's no money in the 'short game' of curing people fast.

My next attempt at sobriety would be "cold turkey." I had given the doctor recommended avenues a try which weren't successful, so now it was time to try it my way. At this point, I had eased up on the drinking, but I was smoking pot like a fiend. Every day, I was smoking when I woke up, smoking through the day, and smoking myself to sleep. I was smoking about an ounce a week, which would have made Cheech and Chong very proud. So, my idea was just to stop and quit

---

[2] Letter from Bill Wilson to Gerald Heard

cold turkey. I was still drinking, so I planned to drink like a fish for a couple of days and get so drunk that I would pass out.

I thought being drunk as hell would keep my mind off the pot, so I went and bought two cases of beer, which was forty-eight beers, and I locked myself inside my apartment. The first day wasn't bad; I drank about eighteen beers and passed out, which I considered a success for day one, as I didn't smoke any pot! The next day I was so hungover I couldn't drink; I just laid around all day feeling like a bag of shit. Since I rested all day, it was tough to fall asleep that night. I didn't sleep at all the second night and day three is where shit got weird. I sat around in a haze all day, and when I went to bed, I was exhausted. I thought I would be able to sleep like a baby, not so. I was able to fall asleep, but I woke up a couple of hours later scared to hell. I had actually dreamed and remembered it, this never happened when I was smoking pot, either I didn't dream, or I didn't remember it, I'm not sure which it is, but it was so vivid, it felt so real, that it was scary as hell. I dreamt I was surrounded by fire, maybe in hell, surrounded by pot plants and joints burning everywhere.

I woke up in a pool of sweat; the bed, all my sheets, and pillows were soaking wet. I sat up, and I could see sweat pouring off my forehead; I've never seen that much sweat coming out of my pores, even sitting in a sauna; I have never seen so much liquid coming out of me. I was freezing, boiling hot, and shivering all at the same time. I couldn't control or stop the shaking; it was as if my whole core was cold and freezing like I had hypothermia. Needless to say, I called my pot guy in the morning. I couldn't go through that again (but of course

I would). Over the years, I must have tried to quit a dozen times cold turkey with no success.

The next time I tried to quit, I would give the doctor another shot, but I didn't have insurance this time. So, I made the dreaded call to my family doctor and made an appointment to admit my addictions and failures once again. This time he referred me to C.A.M.H., the Centre for Addiction and Mental Health. This is the government-funded addiction treatment process, and if you are 'lucky' enough to get in, this is where they treat every kind of addiction. When you enter the facility, it's like entering an asylum or a prison; staff and doctors are protected by bars and heavy plexiglass, you are buzzed in, and doors lock behind you as you move through the facility. It's funny how addiction rehabilitation is along the same lines as incarceration in our society. The first step of the process is the 'intake appointment,' where they determine what the best avenue of treatment would be best for you. Basically, it comes down to only two treatment plans; you either get locked up for thirty days with meth heads, heroin addicts, and homeless people with severe mental problems. Or you are recommended for 'group therapy,' where you are assigned to group therapy sessions for sixty to ninety days, with meth heads, heroin addicts, and homeless people with severe mental problems.

I went to one group meeting, and it was scary, just seeing how damaging addiction can be and how far it can drag you down was very sobering. I didn't fit in with that group. I mean, I had a job, an apartment, a car, I was a functioning pothead and alcoholic while everyone else in my group were street junkies, coke heads, and people that would do unthinkable acts for their next fix. I lasted one meeting; it wasn't for me.

My next attempt to quit was one of my ideas, hypnotism! Let me stop you right now if you are thinking of trying this avenue of addiction therapy. This bullshit cost me one thousand dollars for ten sessions, so let me save you some money. Get up, go to your bathroom, flush five hundred dollars down the toilet, and you will still be five hundred dollars ahead. After doing this, I know how charlatans can make a living. I was desperate to quit and was looking for anything to help me, and these folks were more than happy to take my money. Hypnotism consists of sitting in a room, listening to soothing sounds through headphones, wearing sunglasses that flash different color lights into your eyes, and listening to the 'therapist' talk in a soft relaxing tone, telling you that you should quit. In my opinion, these guys were good; they were good at hustling people out of their money but not curing people. I did everything the guy told me to do, I had an open mind at the time, and it was utterly useless. You are better off buying a ten-dollar book on meditation, a cd of soothing sounds, meditating, and relaxing on your terms, and the cost? No more than fifty bucks.

After my car accident, I was prescribed oxycontin to help me with the physical aspect of rehabilitation. Unfortunately, I developed a dependency on them, and it was another addiction I had to quit and deal with. Thankfully, I was still smoking pot when I needed to stop taking the pills as it became my next idea that I could quit one substance by replacing it with another. When it was time to quit the oxy, I bought two ounces of pot and hunkered down at my Uncle Johnny's place. When I stopped taking them, my mind went to some dark and scary places; I felt so weak and scared that I broke down in tears at some points. I stayed up for three days straight and smoked two ounces of pot with my Uncle Johnny until I was able to fall asleep. As I said earlier, I can't thank him enough, he saved my life by helping me quit, and I will always be eternally grateful. Since I had success using a ton of pot to quit taking oxy, it got stuck in my brain that I could quit one substance by replacing it with another, which gave me the idea of how I would try to quit pot the next time.

When I was working at the post office, I decided to try to quit again; I was working as a supervisor, the worst job ever. It was around Christmas when I was given vacation unexpectedly, I had nothing going on, so I decided that I would use the time wisely and try to quit smoking pot. And my idea this time was to get as far away from it as I could. I knew that if I was close to pot and that it was just a phone call away, I would just cave and make the call to pick up. So, I decided to hit the road and drive as far away as possible, but where would I go? I got online and looked at a map; I had two weeks, so I could go anywhere, but where? I wanted to make it a little meaningful and give the trip a little purpose, so I decided to go to the Grand Canyon. I'd never been to the western United States, and I always wanted to see it, so I thought that would be perfect. I looked at the map, and it was twenty-two hundred miles and one international border from Toronto, which should be far enough from pot and my dealers. But I knew I couldn't be sober while I was withdrawing; I still thought I needed a little mind-altering, but I couldn't drink and drive, so what was I going to do? This is where I got the bright idea to grab a couple of grams of coke and drive as far as I could. If I could quit oxycontin smoking pot,

I'm sure I could quit pot by snorting coke! I never told anyone about my plan, well I told them about driving to the Grand Canyon, but I didn't tell them about my idea of doing cocaine to quit pot! I packed my bags, put a set of golf clubs in the trunk as the cover for going down south, and I grabbed two grams of coke and hit the road.

Most people wouldn't think of doing what I did, but I'm not like most people. I had to figure out how I would do this, I couldn't be all bouncy and jittery when I crossed the border, so I had to pace myself. Once I hit the highway, I put the car on cruise control five miles over the speed limit, and I stayed in the right lane. It was bad enough that I was crossing the US-Canadian border with a schedule one narcotic, so the last thing I needed was to be pulled over for speeding or not signaling a lane change. I only snorted a little; I used a key and just did a few key bumps before I got to the border. When I got close to the border, I pulled over stopped at a rest stop to get my shit together. I brought two Ziploc bags to wrap up my little baggy of coke so nothing would smell just in case I was stopped, and the dogs came around. I pulled the golf clubs out of the trunk and dumped them all out of the bag. I taped up the bag of coke then proceeded to tape it to the inside of the golf bag, I put the clubs back in the bag, and I crossed my fingers.

Approaching the border, I must admit I was a little nervous, but I have always been able to talk my way out of situations and make a connection with people when I meet them. It's how I was able to avoid getting arrested for drinking and drugs throughout my life. As I got closer, I put a piece of gum in my mouth and put on my Post Office hat for a little extra help. At the post office, we worked with Customs

Officials who worked in our facilities searching the international mail; there was a 'comradery' between customs employees and 'posties.' As I pulled up to the customs booth, I saw that it was an older lady at the window, perfect! I pulled up, gave her my passport, and she asked the standard questions, "what is your citizenship and what's the purpose of your visit to the United States, business or personal?". I replied, "uh, Canadian and personal." It was at this point that she looked up from her screen, she noticed the hat and asked, "do you work for the post office? Are you a postie?" (The endearing term for employees of the post office). I said, "yes, ma'am, CUPW (the union for posties)," saying the union would help also; it seems there's a brotherhood between unions too. She said, "I have some friends that work in the plant here," I thought, 'of course you do,' it was then I knew I was getting through no problem! I replied, "Yup, I work with some customs folk when I'm in the plant, I never get used to those bomb scares." She smiles and says, "yeah I've heard some stories, so why are you travelling down to the United States all alone at Christmas time, sweetie?" "Well, I got two weeks of vacation at the last minute, I'm single, and I thought I would drive to Arizona, see a friend, visit the Grand Canyon and do some golfing." She said, "well ok then, have a great time, merry Christmas and welcome to the United States." Relieved, I said, "thank you dear, and merry Christmas to you!"

I drove about fifteen minutes to a Denny's parking lot. I got the coke out of the golf bag and did a huge 'Hollywood' line to celebrate! I hit the road, cranked up the tunes, and put the cruise control on, and wondered how far I would get before I shouldn't, or should I say, couldn't drive anymore. I made it to Chicago. Checking into the motel was interesting; I got there around three in the morning and could hardly talk. If you have ever done cocaine, you know what it does to your jaw. I was grinding my teeth so hard I could barely open my mouth to talk. I've always wondered what the clerk thought when she checked me in; I was surprised I could even get a room. When I got to my room, I didn't come out and slept for two days. The remainder of the trip was fantastic, driving from one city to another, getting Starbucks in the mornings and beers at night, not knowing where I was going or where I was going to end up. I made it to the Grand Canyon on Christmas Day, and the hotel was empty. It was a ghost town; the only person in the lobby was the cute native American hotel clerk. She was the only one I had seen for three days; on the last night, she was sympathetic that I was traveling alone at Christmas time, she took pity on me, and we spent the night together; the Grand Canyon was amazing. No one was at the Grand Canyon on the days I went there, and on the last day I was there, it snowed; it was awesome; it was one of the best trips of my life. It was also one of the most successful attempts of quitting I have ever had. I had stopped smoking pot for about two months after that trip, the longest I have ever been able to go without getting high! But back at the post office in a job that I hated, I just started smoking and drinking again to numb myself from the reality I hated.

I would try quitting a couple of years later, this time with doctor assistance one more time, and I decided to give a psychiatrist one last chance, but I wasn't insured. My family doctor referred me to a local hospitals' mental health and addiction unit. This is where the doctors treating people are government employees. Remember when I previously said that you get good treatment when the doctor cares for you? This is the treatment plan where you end up seeing a doctor who doesn't give a shit about you; they have the security of a government job and are un-fireable. This bitch was like any other government employee in their job, there to do just enough to get by and make it through the day. I gave her the benefit of the doubt, but she had blue hair at the first appointment I attended. The second appointment, she had pink hair, and we got in a fight, not about the hair, but because when she was reviewing the last appointment with me, she stated that she referred me to group therapy. I replied, "oh no, you didn't refer me to anything", I was sure of this because if she had, I would have been apprehensive about working it into my schedule and having to go to yet more appointments. She lost it on me, started arguing and yelling at me that she did, saying she was sure she did, and she started criticizing me. I knew what was going on; it was part of her job, it was what she was supposed to do, but I knew she was lazy as fuck and didn't give a crap about me. It wasn't a big deal to me. I didn't care, but I resented how she went off on me because I knew she was just trying to cover her ass. I didn't care about it until she tried to use the authority against me, but the way she behaved, you would have thought she was the one there for therapy. She dismissed me and scheduled another appointment. I had no intention of going back, but as I said, I wanted to give quitting another serious try, and I was giving her the benefit of the doubt.

When I showed up for the next appointment, I was booked for work later in the day, so I was pressed for time. We had previously discussed how hard it was for me to get into appointments with her because of my work schedule. When she walked in twenty minutes late and was unapologetic for it, I was pissed off, and I was done with this lazy government waste of taxpayers' money, and oh yeah, this time she came in with green hair. I was going to get up and leave, but then I decided this disrespectful bitch needed to be told what I thought of her. I asked her why she was late? She replied, "I don't need to answer to you, things happen, people have busy schedules". I didn't miss a beat and replied instantly, "That shows tremendous disrespect and a total lack of unprofessionalism to the person waiting for you, and I bet you wouldn't keep your boss or someone of a higher position waiting, just people that you looked down on, that shows horrible character." I was talking right at her. She couldn't even look up at me. I asked "how come your hair is green this time? Can't make up your mind what color you want?" She looked up and said, "I like to color it to see what other peoples' reactions are, see what their thoughts are and how they react." Now, I used to hang around with punks and skinheads, people with mohawks and spikes before it was cool to do. Now, I work with many artists, singers, musicians, and actors, and I know all of them do it for themselves and how it makes them feel, so I wasn't going to hold back on this loser. I said, "you do it for other people? That is so pathetic; what kind of insecure loser dyes their hair for other peoples' reactions and not for what it does to you on the inside, what kind of personality trait is that doc?" She looked at me with her jaw wide in disbelief. I asked, "who's the crazy one in this room?" "I don't think that's an appropriate question", she finally replied. I said, "I think it is. It's exactly appropriate, you are here as the mental health professional, but I think your mental health is in question, and if it's not, then it seems like you don't give a shit about the people you are treating and are here just to punch the clock, get your paycheck and make it to your pension. If you are mentally stable and this is your level of professionalism, then you should just retire or die, I don't care which, because people come here for your help and the way you treat people is horrible. Also, someone as old as you, with hair like that just looks sad, and you look like a joke. I honestly don't think I should take any advice from you in your condition as I believe you are the one with serious problems". She just sat there staring at me as I smiled and told her what I thought. I stood up, wished her the best of luck, and left. It was the last time I would ever have faith in our mental health system and the last time I would ever think I needed help from a psychiatrist.

Since I decided I was done with doctors for my depression and addiction, I thought the least I could do was show my family doctor some respect and discuss my plan for psychedelic therapy with him. He was prescribing me Cipralex and Ativan at the time, and though I felt they were ineffective for helping, he had always been there for me and very supportive of me through the years, so I thought it best to keep him in the loop. I wasn't sure how receptive he would be with me quitting the prescriptions and going down the psychedelic route, so I wasn't too sure how to handle this. He's a very traditional and 'by the book' kind of doctor, so I didn't think he would be too excited for my plan. When I went in, I chickened out; I didn't have the courage to tell him about it, so I decided I would just ask him questions and feel him out on his attitude toward psychedelics. My first step was asking him if he thinks that the pills I'm taking are working. I explained that I have been taking them on and off for half of my life, and not much has changed. I still have bouts of depression, I still smoke a shitload of pot daily to deal with my PTSD, and I still get drunk a lot, so what's really the point of the pills? He replied, "well, at least you are getting out of bed in the morning, the world isn't as dark as it was for you, and it seems like you are functioning." I replied, "Well, I'm barely functioning, I'm still a chronic pothead, and I still drink like a fish."

This is where I asked him the magic question, "Hey doc, what are your thoughts' about psychedelic treatment for depression and addiction, you know psilocybin, LSD, or DMT?". His answer didn't surprise me. "Well, those are very dangerous substances, and if not used right, they can be very harmful. I'm not familiar with what's been going on in that field." I then asked him, "have you ever taken mushrooms or acid?" "No never, I would never touch things like that. I had to ask, "well then, how do you know how dangerous or harmful they are?" This, of course, got his back up. He asked, "Why do you ask?". "Well, I have been doing a lot of reading about how they are starting to research psychedelics for addiction and depression therapy." When he asked, "where have you been reading this, on the internet? You'll read a lot of disinformation online". All I could say was, "Well doc, it seems like a lot of prestigious and respectable institutions are starting to explore and research them for treatment. There are even some stocks in the psychedelic sector now." He asked me once again. "Why are you asking?" I replied, "No reason, I was just curious." "Well, don't do anything stupid without consulting me," he wrote me the prescriptions and I was on my way. I was a little upset when I left the doctor's office; I felt as if I knew more than the doctor about the subject. Here was a guy telling me what to do when he has never even tried them nor ever read anything on psychedelics. Yes, he's a doctor, but he has absolutely no experience and no knowledge of the subject, yet he has no problem acting like he knows more. He just knows the lies that Government and Society have told him all his life. I was a little mad when I left his office, and as I left the office, I threw the prescriptions in the garbage. I was on my way to do something 'stupid.'

Why I Don't Trust the Government About Psychedelics.

This is where I might lose you, but what I'm going to tell you might open your eyes and might change the way you think about your government. I'm going to talk about the government and their mind control program 'MK Ultra'[3], their involvement with psychedelics, and why I don't trust a word they say about them. When I started writing this book, I thought I knew how the world worked, and I believed my government when they told me things. But this book has opened a lot of rabbit holes for me and as I started researching various topics, I would be lead down different paths. One of the paths I went down was

---

[3]Joint Hearing before the Select Committee Intelligence and the Sub Committee on Health and Scientific Research of the Committee on Human Resources United States Senate. www.intelligence.senate.gov August 3, 1977

about government projects/operations that the general population would call conspiracy theory. One such program I came across early in the research that opened my eyes and showed me that the government tells its population one thing while doing another was 'Operation Paperclip'[4]; this showed me how the government lies to its people.

'Operation Paperclip' was a program that was in effect from nineteen forty-five to nineteen fifty-nine. It was responsible for giving clemency and pardoning over sixteen hundred Nazi/German engineers, technicians, doctors, and scientists, some of whom were experimenting in torture and mind control. The operation was run by the then Director of the CIA, Allen Dulles. Its goal was to bring these war criminals and their families to the United States. The US government forgave these men for whatever their participation was in the war in exchange for their knowledge, and they were given new lives. While the government was busy putting on the most significant propaganda trials of the century, the trials of Nuremberg, where two hundred Nazis were tried for war crimes, behind the public's view, they were busy with 'Operation Paperclip.' The most notable person they forgave, gave a new life and salary to was Wernher von Braun[5] and his V2 rocket team. The 'V2' rocket was responsible for killing thousands and blowing the hell out of England; this was all forgiven. Heck, Nasa could be called the 'Nazi Aeronautics and Space Administration' because so many Germans were imported and began working for them. Though 'Operation Paperclip' was eventually exposed and brought to

---

[4] 'Operation Paperclip – The Secret Intelligence Program That Brought Nazi Scientists to America' Annie Jacobsen 2014

[5] 'How Historians Are Reckoning with the Former Nazi Who Launched Americas Space Program' Time Magazine, 2019 Alejandro De La Garza

the public's attention, most of the people I discuss this with have no idea about it, and say "isn't that just conspiracy theory?"

Upon learning about 'Operation Paperclip,' I realized that things might not be as they seem or that what we 'think' we know, may not be the truth. So, at the end of this chapter, I list a few more things that the government may not want you to know and have all been called 'conspiracy theory', a term coined by the CIA after the Kennedy Assassination to negate any opinions that went against the official narrative[6]. But one thing that is true and deemed to be 'conspiracy theory' for many years, until proven true, was the project 'MK Ultra,' the government program of mind control which they denied and said was just another 'conspiracy theory' until it was proven to be true. That's what I'll be talking about, and it is why I don't trust the government regarding psychedelics or anything else for that matter[7].

After WWII and the Korean War, Prisoner of War soldiers returned to America, and some were returning against their will. The US discovered that the communists were torturing and subjecting American soldiers to brainwashing techniques while they were prisoners of war. This gave the CIA the excuse to develop and fund projects 'Operation Bluebird' and 'Operation Artichoke,' which were born out of 'Operation Paperclip' and grew into project 'MK Ultra.' Yes, the same project that brought Nazis doctors and scientists to America was the same project that was ultimately responsible for

---

[6] Conspiracy Theory in America' Lance DeHaven-Smith, 2013

[7] Joint Hearing before the Select Committee Intelligence and the Sub Committee on Health and Scientific Research of the Committee on Human Resources United States Senate. www.intelligence.senate.gov August 3, 1977

project 'MK Ultra,' it makes you wonder where they learned and developed some of these mind control and torture techniques.

Project 'MK Ultra' consisted of over one hundred and forty sub-projects experimenting with sensory deprivation techniques, hypnotism, torture, and drugs to get people to commit acts that were inherently against their human nature and leave them with no recollection of those acts. A program to create the ultimate subservient soldier, an actual 'Manchurian Candidate.'

MK Ultra started in nineteen fifty-three for about a decade until nineteen sixty-four. It was initiated by the then Director of the CIA, Allen Dulles (friend of Heimlich Himmler), headed by Deputy Director Richard Helms. Helms put CIA head chemist Sidney Gottlieb, who was already familiar with torture and chemical warfare, in charge of the clandestine program. This program wasn't publicly known until nineteen seventy-five when the Senate held the Church Committee Hearings responsible for investigating "Government Operations with Respect to Intelligence Activities." During this hearing, they discovered all the documents on MK Ultra were ordered to be destroyed by Helms and Gottlieb. In nineteen seventy-three, in the wake of the "Watergate" scandal, Helms and Gottlieb, who were leaving the CIA, knew that if the true nature of these experiments came to light, it wouldn't be good for either of them.

It wasn't until nineteen seventy-seven when a Freedom of Information request discovered about twenty thousand documents relating to MK Ultra were sent to the 'Financial Archives Office' and survived the destruction orders, which brought to light some of the horrors of the MK Ultra program to the public eye. We learned of these programs not because the government finally got a conscience and decided it was in the people's best interest to tell them; it was because they were caught in their twisted abuse of unknowing subjects.

In nineteen fifty-three, Sidney Gottlieb was worried that the Soviets had a superior mind-controlling drug in their possession. This drug was Lysergic Acid Diethylamide, or better known as LSD, a synthetic drug created in nineteen forty-eight in a Swiss laboratory by chemist Albert Hoffman, the father of LSD. Hoffman discovered a molecule that was derived from a rare fungus developed from ergot mold. After accidentally having some absorbed in his skin and after taking a trippy bike ride home from the lab, Hoffman discovered the molecule had psychotropic effects that could be used in the field of psychiatry. He found this drug could severely alter a persons' perception and thoughts. This was very interesting to the biological and chemical weapons divisions of governments. Wanting to make sure the Soviets didn't get ahead of the US in this field, Gottleib arranged to purchase the entire worlds' supply of LSD from Sandoz Laboratories and brought it to America. Yes, ladies and gentlemen, we can thank the CIA and US Government for bringing LSD into our culture and ultimately being responsible for the psychedelic counterculture of the sixties, the movement which the government would eventually end up despising and fearing, ironic isn't it?

During my journey down the rabbit hole of MK Ultra and the government, what shocked me was some of the events and the twisted, sick people involved, all in the name 'science.' One such event was the death of Frank Olsen. Olsen was an employee of the CIA who specialized in developing aerosol sprays for the delivery deployment of anthrax (a fact that will be important later). Olsen mysteriously fell to his death from a hotel window in nineteen fifty-three while a CIA escort was present in the room[8]. Earlier in the year, Sidney Gottlieb had slipped Olsen a dose of LSD during a meeting, and a few days after that, Olsen tried to resign and retire from the CIA; his reason, he said, he had regrets about his participation in the CIA. Gottlieb sent him to New York with a CIA escort to meet with a psychiatrist and a magician, yes, a magician. Both were on the payroll of the CIA, and they determined he needed to be institutionalized even though his wife said that he was in good spirits and looked forward to returning home when they spoke the night, he supposedly killed himself. It wasn't until many years later that Olsen's son, Erik, claimed there was evidence that his father was murdered. When Secret Services investigator Hank Albarelli Jr began to research Olsen's death, it was determined there was, in fact, wrongdoing. The government ended up paying the family seven hundred and fifty thousand dollars in nineteen seventy-six to avoid any litigation regarding his death[9]. Why I mention this story is because I found it so offensive, that not only did they not care about the general population, but that they didn't even care about their own.

Gottlieb had carte blanche and free reign to do whatever he felt necessary in Project MK Ultra, and he did exactly that. He unleashed LSD and mind control experiments on knowing and unknowing soldiers, civilians, hospital patients, and prisoners. For over ten years, he oversaw one hundred and forty sub-projects of MK Ultra[10], with no

---

[8] "What Did the CIA Do To His Father" Michael Ignatieff, New York Times April 2001

[9] "What Did the CIA Do To His Father" Michael Ignatieff, New York Times April 2001

[10] Joint Hearing Before the Select Committee on Intelligence and Scientific Research, 1977

supervision or anyone asking any questions. He recruited prisons, hospitals, and universities all over the country who didn't even know they were doing experiments for the CIA. They even funded programs outside of the United States, their reasoning for this was that the program would be more convoluted. There would be fewer repercussions for them, and a less likely chance they would get caught and exposed for the US Government torturing civilians. If experiments were done in a foreign country, and a foreign country is torturing its citizens, who really is to blame? And Canada was perfect and compliant for doing just that. Money for these projects was funneled through different front organizations such as 'The Human Ecology Foundation.' This way, there could always be some confusion or deniability of who these institutions were actually working for.

One of the Sub Projects and most brutal documented in the 'Church Committee Hearings' [11] was subproject sixty-eight, which took place at McGill University in Montreal. McGill was chosen because of their previous experiments in sensory deprivation, which turned out to be very effective torture techniques. The experiments took place at McGill's' Allen Memorial Institute, headed by Dr. Ewan Cameron, an American, a world-renowned, highly respected psychiatrist. He even served as President of the Canadian, American and World Psychiatry Associations. Dr. Cameron's subjects were fifty-three innocent people that were psychiatric patients of the hospital who were unknowing participants in the experiments they were taking part in. But because he was the 'world-renowned' and the 'highly respected' Dr. Cameron, they

---

[11] Senate Church Committee Hearings, 1975

assumed he had their best interests at heart; he didn't. His goal was to wipe his patients' minds clean using a technique called 'psychic driving' which consisted of daily electro-shock therapy, listening to the same subliminal message for over a quarter of a million times through a football helmet locked to their head, all the while he dosed them with large amounts of LSD daily. He would drug his patients asleep for upwards of thirty to forty DAYS at a time. He administered his patients Artane, a heavy tranquilizer that was experimental and extremely dangerous. He experimented with 'Anectine,' a paralyzing inducing toxin; he used a tranquilizer used by Pigmies, who would dip their arrows in the poison to induce paralysis in their victims, he administered 'Bulbocapnine' another experimental paralyzer; and he even gave his patients PCP. He went further with drugs and electro-shock therapy than any other doctor in the MK Ultra program. These experiments caused irreparable and life-long damage to the test subjects and even caused one patient to commit suicide.

Surviving victims filed a lawsuit against the Canadian government for their involvement with letting the torture take place. Only one person received compensation through an out-of-court settlement, and the Canadian government never acknowledged or admitted to knowing what was going on, so the original plan of experiments taking place outside of the USA worked and was effective for the CIA[12]. In the nineteen-eighties, the Canadian news show 'The Fifth Estate' uncovered and interviewed the surviving victims, who to this day, still have not received an apology or admission from the

---

[12] Joint Hearing Before the Select Committee on Intelligence and Scientific Research, 1977

spineless Canadian government [13]. And just as an FYI, do you think it is a coincidence that Dr. Cameron was sent to the 'Trials of Nuremberg's to examine Rudolf Hess? Rudolph Hess was the Nazi doctor who performed horrific experiments on people in the concentration camps. And what was the Government narrative of what Dr. Cameron discovered and recorded into the 'Nuremberg Code'? "Subjects of experiments must give their full consent to any experimentation." Yup, the government will always tell us the truth.

One of the more twisted and deviant sub-programs of MK Ultra was sub-project 3, 'Operation Midnight Climax.' This sub-project involved sex and LSD. Sidney Gottlieb put CIA operative George Hunter White in charge. White set up brothels and recruited prostitutes in New York and San Francisco that he would use to conduct the 'experiments' (if you can call them that). The prostitutes would bring the 'Johns' back to the brothel where they would be unknowingly slipped 'LSD' while engaging in intercourse with them. The intention was to see what men would say or confess to after sex and under the influence of the drug. The real twisted part was that White would sit behind two-way mirrors drinking martini's watching the girls and 'johns,' all in the name of science. Not only did the government buy the drugs, but they also paid for the girls and all the expenses that went into running the bordellos! Operation Midnight Climax was documented in witness testimony and financial documents uncovered in the Senate Hearings.[14]

---

[13] 'Group Affected by CIA Brainwashing Experiments Wants Public Apology from Government' Lisa Ellenwood CBC News

[14] Joint Hearing Before the Select Committee on Intelligence and Scientific Research, 1977

Other programs that involved unwitting participants included the Menlo Park Veterans hospital where Ken Kessey, author of 'One Flew Over the Cuckoos' Nest,' took part; Kessey would also be part of 'The Merry Pranksters.' They were a group of psychedelic pioneers that traveled the country spreading the word of psychedelics and LSD itself[15]. Stanford University where Robert Hunter, lyricist for the 'Grateful Dead,' was a participant; Harvard University where the infamous Unabomber Ted Kaczynski was a participant; and many prisons where criminals were asked to participate in return for good behavior. One such prisoner was Whitey Bulger, who was told by University Professor Dr. Carl Pfeiffer of Emory University that he was participating in an experiment for a schizophrenic medication. Mr. Bulger said he was injected daily with LSD, studied and questioned by men dressed in suits that were obviously not doctors. Interrogation style questions like, 'have you ever killed a man? Would you kill a man?' He says the program almost drove him insane, and it wouldn't be until years later that he found out he was unwittingly a participant in MK Ultra, something he said that he never recovered from[16].

One of the last horror stories of psychedelic abuse that the government may have unleashed under the guise of 'experiments' is the story of the small French town 'Point Saint-Esprit.' There is no concrete evidence, and nothing was ever confirmed; there's only a couple of huge coincidences that are too big to ignore. In nineteen fifty-one, over three hundred people in the small town suffered hallucinations and bouts of madness. There were stories of people

---

[15] 'The Electric Kool-Aid Acid Test Tom Wolfe, 1968

[16] 'The Whitey Bulger Notebook.'

jumping out of windows, people having horrific, nightmarish visions, and even seeing demons. Seven people died, and over fifty people were admitted to psychiatric wards. To this day, there has been no definitive reason for this outbreak, but there are two theories. After being interviewed, it turned out that all the people affected had purchased bread at the 'Briand Bakery.' It is thought that the bread had gone bad and developed Grain Ergot, which resulted in the poisoning, which would explain why people hallucinated and had bouts of madness.

Now here's where the coincidences are too much to ignore. The authorities called in Dr. Albert Hoffman, the Father of LSD to investigate, and it was in his opinion that this outbreak had all the signs and was most definitely, undoubtedly, the effects of LSD poisoning. But when French authorities wanted to follow up with Dr. Hoffman, he refused to speak with them and would put nothing on the record. The next colossal coincidence that is too big to ignore, is that Frank Olsen (remember, he specialized in aerosol sprays of chemical weapons) was in Point St. Esprit just months before the outbreak. This was discovered by Hank Albarelli while investigating Olsen's death and could have been what Olsen was deeply regretting and was why he tried to resign. An experiment like this is not outside the possibility of government actions[17]. In nineteen fifty-five, the CIA conducted open-air tests of the whooping cough bacteria over Florida. They were testing the spreading of chemical weapons using aerosols, and this resulted in cases of whooping cough increasing from three hundred and thirty-nine to one thousand and eighty with twelve deaths[18]. Just in

---

[17] 'Point-Saint-Esprit' Poisoning: Did the CIA Spread LSD BBC News, August 23, 2010

[18] 'Report Suggests CIA Involvement in FLA. Illnesses' Washington Post, December 17, 1979

case you were wondering if they were capable of something like Point St, Esprit.

Just so you don't think I'm a total cynic, I want to talk about the good things that happened with psychedelics before the government used scientific evidence to decide what would be best for us regarding psychedelics. And if you thought I was serious saying scientific evidence, I wasn't, you'll see their decision to ban psychedelics was purely political. When LSD was created, not only was it noticed by our twisted Governments, but it was also noticed by some psychiatrists and doctors that recognized the potential benefits of this drug.

In the nineteen fifties (Pre MK Ultra), a psychiatrist named Humphrey Osmond was working in the psychiatric department of St. Georges Hospital in London. He learned of Albert Hoffman's discovery of LSD at the Sandoz Pharmaceutical Company in Basel, Switzerland. In nineteen fifty-one, he moved to Saskatchewan, Canada, and brought some LSD back with him. He began doing some experiments at the Weyburn Mental Hospital with his colleague Abram Hoffer and bless his heart, he even tried it himself. One of the experiments consisted of giving a group of hardcore alcoholics one high dose of LSD. The results were very positive: one-third kept drinking, one-third stayed sober for six to twelve months, and one-third quit drinking forever. He concluded that the drug could produce profound changes in a person's consciousness. Through their experiments, they theorized that the drug could create new levels of self-awareness in a person, which could have tremendous potential in the world of psychiatry. They tried an experiment on two alcoholics and gave them each a mega-dose of two hundred mg of LSD, one stopped drinking the very next day, and the other stopped six months later. Years later, Osmond met Aldous Huxley, who was experimenting with mescaline at the time and would coin the term 'psychedelic' in a letter to his friend Aldous Huxley, a proponent and user of mescalin who would later pen the great novels 'Brave New World' and 'The Doors of Perception.

In the 1950's, proper scientific trials and experiments were not only happening in Canada. They were going on in the US and Europe, and the results were similar; psychedelics were helping cure alcoholism and making great strides in depression and psychotherapy treatment. It was starting to pick up momentum, LSD therapy was breaking through to the mainstream, participants included Ethel Kennedy (Bobby's wife) and Cary Grant, who was a big advocate of LSD therapy. LSD therapy was also endorsed by Alcoholics Anonymous co-founder Bill Wilson who was also Director of Saskatchewan's Bureau on Alcoholism. There were two forms of treatment experimented with, one consisting of a single large dose, and another composed of several smaller quantities, precisely what is being brought to fruition today, 'mega' and 'micro-dosing.'

During the nineteen-fifties and early sixties, over forty thousand patients had been prescribed one form of LSD therapy or another for conditions ranging from neurosis, alcoholism, schizophrenia, psychotherapy, and even given to children with autism. Over one thousand scientific papers were written in these years, and there were even international conferences to discuss LSD therapies. Early findings concluded that there were tremendous benefits to the psychedelic treatment, and it was thought that this treatment would be the next big breakthrough in psychiatry, even surpassing electro-shock and psychosurgery[19]. In addition, they discovered that inducing dreamlike hallucinations that went deep into the patients' unconscious mind would enable people to relive long-lost or repressed memories. But what happened? Why was something with such promise shut down and demonized? Once the government got involved with psychedelics, everything went wrong.

Also, in the nineteen fifties, George Wasson, a self-proclaimed ethnomycologist, author, and VP of Public Relations at J.P Morgan and a botanist by the name of Roger Heim, took an expedition to Mexico in search of the 'sacred mushroom.' While in Mexico, they met Maria Sabrina, a Mazatec Shaman who used the sacred mushroom for its healing and spiritual effects. To the locals, psychedelic mushrooms were called 'the flesh of the gods.' She introduced Wasson to the mushroom, something she later said she deeply regretted. I would also like to note Maria Sabina deserves a whole book to herself. She was a beautiful, spiritual woman who used the mushroom to better her people; she was deeply spiritually in touch with nature and this world. It is just unfortunate that her path crossed with Wesson's.

History would reveal that Wesson's' trip was funded by the CIA under Project MK Ultra, sub-project 58, and funded by a foundation called "Geshickter Fund for Medical Research." After all, you don't work for one of the companies/families that created the Federal Reserve without having deep, deep government connections. In

---

[19] 'A Brief History of Psychedelic Psychiatry' The Guardian, Mo Costandi, Sept 5, 2014

nineteen fifty-seven, an article appeared in Life Magazine titled, 'Seeking the Magic Mushroom' [20]. This was when the term "Magic Mushroom" was coined, and it is when the disservice and stigma of the mushroom began. So not only was the US Government responsible for bringing LSD to North America, the Government, was also responsible for introducing the Western World to the sacred mushroom and psilocybin. I guess we owe them thanks for that!

Besides the torture and mind control experiments that were taking place at Harvard under the MK Ultra project, there were also some psychedelic experiments taking place, two professors running such experiments were Richard Alpert and Timothy Leary. You may not recognize the first name, but I am sure you recognize the second. Leary was dubbed the 'Pioneer of the Psychedelic Movement,' when he should have been dubbed 'the destroyer of the psychedelic movement.' He and his colleague created the 'Psilocybin Project,' whose board of directors included none other than Aldous Huxley, author of 'Brave New World' and 'The Doors of Perception. It is not known if the 'Psilocybin Project' was funded by the CIA, but there is a strong chance it was. The project didn't last long as Leary was taking part in it as much as his students. The project was shut down when Leary's fellow professors questioned the validity of the study. The project disbanded, and Leary left Harvard to become the 'de facto leader' of the sixties 'counter-culture,' dubbed the 'High Priest of LSD'. Though he really did believe that psychedelics had great therapeutic potential, he just went about promoting them in the wrong and destructive way. He

---

[20] Secret of the Divine Mushrooms Life Magazine, George Wasson, May 13, 1957

publicly promoted the use of psychedelic in society and created the phrases "Turn On, Tune In, and Drop Out!" and "think for yourself and question authority" now, these slogans and phrases were not popular with the authorities and the people in power. It didn't help that Leary befriended groups like the 'Weathermen,' a radical left-wing militant organization that is said to have helped Leary escape from prison and people like Eldridge Cleaver, the early leader of the Black Panther Party. Leary was also associated with the "Brotherhood of Eternal Love," a group whose goal was to spread the message of marijuana and psychedelics throughout America. Psychedelics became associated with the anti-war movement and the 'counter-culture' which scared the establishment so much that Richard Nixon would call Timothy Leary the most dangerous man in America and dubbed him 'public enemy number one' [21]. Leary would be tossed in jail multiple times and once even sharing a cell with Charles Manson. It was never proved that Leary was ever working for the CIA, and he always denied it, but Leary credits the CIA for supplying the LSD that led to the psychedelic movement of the sixties[22].

In nineteen sixty-two, the UN updated their nineteen thirty-one Convention on substances to include modern synthetic opioid substances and marijuana creations. In nineteen seventy-one they created the Convention on Psychotropic Substances to contain the newly created and discovered psychedelic substances. This banned and limited any further research into psychedelics and made it impossible to

[21] The Most Dangerous Man in America: Timothy Leary, Richard Nixon, and the Hunt for the Fugitive King of LSD Bill Minutaglio, 2018
[22] The Electric Kool-Aid Acid Test, Tom Wolfe

continue[23]. Then to make it worst, in nineteen seventy Richard Nixon created the Controlled Substances Act, thus creating the US drug policy and starting the war on drugs[24]. In this act, schedule one included highly addictive drugs such as heroin, drugs with a potential for abuse, drugs without any accepted medical use, and drugs that were unsafe to use under medical supervision. In this act, mushrooms, and marijuana, were included in Schedule 1. All previous research and past advancements of psychedelics and marijuana were dismissed and ignored. This act made it illegal to import, manufacture, distribute and even possess any of these substances, so now psychedelics and marijuana were in the same classification as heroin. The irony, hypocrisy, and utter nonsense of the act was that drugs like amphetamines, fentanyl, and even methamphetamines were considered less potent being placed on schedule two. This prompted prominent and respected politician Bobby Kennedy, whose wife Ethyl had been taking LSD therapies, to question the validity of the act by asking, "how can we ignore the promise that these drugs had six months ago, and now claim them as dangerous?" They were deemed dangerous because they threatened the establishment. What would have been good for the people and make them smarter was not good for the alcohol and pharmaceutical industries and the powers that run our society.

Like George Carlin said, "Governments don't want a population capable of critical thinking; they want obedient workers,

---

[23] UN Convention on Psychotropic Substances 1973 UN Convention on Psychotropic Substances 1973

[24] Controlled Substances Act (CSA) of 1970

people just smart enough to run the machines and just dumb enough to passively accept their position."[25] So, disregarding the doctor's and scientist's opinions of psychedelics, the government and establishment made them illegal because they threatened their political system. Therefore, I don't trust the government regarding psychedelics or anything else for that matter.

PS. Here are some other instances that I have learned about that reinforce my opinion. You can look them up at your convenience: Gulf of Tonkin Incident, the Tuskegee Experiments, Operation Cointelpro, Operation Northwoods, Operation Fast & Furious, Operation Mockingbird, Iran-Contra, Citizens for a Free Kuwait PR Group, Canadian Residential Schools, Bohemian Grove, Project Azorian, Anthrax & The Prep Act, Iraq with WMD's, Project Sunshine, Waco, Building 7, Chicago Black Sites, the Opioid Crisis, Cocaine/Crack Epidemic and every other false flag operation we may not be aware of yet. And oh yeah, why haven't they released the JFK Assassination Archives yet? Anyway, I digress, please, do your own research and draw your own conclusions.

---

[25] George Carlin 'The American Dream', 2010

Micro and Mega Dosing.

I'm going to be honest, as I said, I am not a doctor of any sort, but I have been under their care and prescribed anti-depressants and therapies since my twenties. I don't know the exact science of how psychedelics affect the mind; I'm not that smart. I have read many books and studies, but I still don't really know what happens chemically inside the brain; I just know it re-wires us somehow. I will try to explain in general, but if you want to know more about the actual science, I suggest reading '*Quantum Science of Psychedelics: The Pineal Gland, Multi-Dimensional Reality and Mayan Cosmology*' *by Carl Johan Callemen 2020 and 'Psychedelic Medicine: The Healing Powers of LSD, MDMA, Psilocybin and Ayahuasca' by Richard Louis Miller 2019.* Or you can seek out a psychedelic clinic that can help you and offer explanations from a trained professional. The following is just a rudimentary explanation of what I learned and what I understand about the brain and psychedelics, it is just my personal 'take away' from what I read from different sources, and as you will see, I am obviously not a doctor, I can only relay what I learned, and how I interpreted it.

It is said that when you have a psychedelic experience, you experience a loss of your ego. It is believed that you lose touch with who you are, which is more commonly called the 'death of the ego,' making you feel good. I genuinely believe that a person's ego dies while they are tripping. I believe mushrooms or psychedelics bring people back to nature, mushrooms humble them, and I feel they make people realize that the world is not all about them that they share this world with other beings. Two studies were carried out by David Nutt, from the Department of Medicine at Imperial College London[26] that examined peoples' brains on psilocybin while in an MRI machine. Previously, it was thought that psychedelics increased activity in certain parts of the brain. At the same time, this might be true for some sections, but they found the activity decreased in certain areas, specifically, the medial prefrontal cortex (mPFC) and the posterior cingulate cortex (PCC). The mPFC is very active in depression, and the PCC is said to be a factor in consciousness and a person's self-identity (ego). This could explain why psilocybin has anti-depressant effects and why peoples' egos are stripped away from them when tripping.

One of the sections also affected by psychedelics is the pineal gland; many people and cultures consider it our biological and spiritual third eye. Science doesn't fully understand the biological or spiritual function of the pineal gland. It is at the geometric center of the brain, and its shape resembles a pinecone hence the name 'pine' al gland. It is

---

[26] New England Journal of Medicine April 2021

linked to our body's perception of light and dark, modulates our waking/sleeping patterns, and regulates our circadian rhythm, which regulates menstrual cycles, digestion, depression, mood, and many other body functions. It's part of the endocrine system, regulating growth, metabolism, sexual development, controlling hormones, and connecting to the nervous system. It is made up of cone and rod 'shaped' cells, like in the eye that receives signals that travel through the optic nerves, hence 'third eye.' The pineal gland receives a large amount of blood flow, making it susceptible to chemicals like psychedelics and toxins that can harm it, such as aluminum and fluoride. Fluoride causes calcification of the gland, influencing diseases like Alzheimer's, cardiovascular disease, autism, eating disorders, and depression. This is why I won't drink tap water or any fluorinated water. The Pineal Gland also produces N-dimethyltryptamine, which is referred to as the 'spirit molecule,' but more commonly known as DMT; surprised?

Pinecones have been used throughout many cultures to symbolize wisdom and insight because of their resemblance to the pineal gland. They can be found in Hindu mythology, Egyptian mythology in the eye of Horus, and the Eye of Ra, in images of Sumerian Gods and is also found in Greek mythology. You will also find a statue of a pinecone at the Vatican. This is not a coincidence. I believe that the pineal gland controls us more than we will ever know. To consume a toxin that will hamper and harm it like fluoride does humanity a huge disservice; you must ask yourself, 'why is a poison put in our drinking water? To protect our teeth?'.

My mental health diagnosis over the years was that I had a chemical imbalance in my brain, I didn't produce enough serotonin, and I was always prescribed serotonin anti-depressants, SSRI medication. For those that aren't aware, serotonin is a monoamine transmitter, and it is responsible for modulating a persons' memory, cognition, learning, and, most importantly, mood. The simple way I explain it is, it's the juice in your brain responsible for how you feel; I call it 'happy juice.' When people would ask about my depression, I would never detail my PTSD or manic moments, I would just say, "I don't have enough 'happy juice' in my head".

From what I have read and understand, hallucinogens stimulate the serotonin 2a receptor in the brain. The hallucinogens stimulate the receptor by mimicking the actions of serotonin on this receptor which alters the internal conditions and, therefore, this behavior of the neuron it sits on. From what I understand, simply put, this is the re-wiring of the brain; they get your impulses firing on receptors that weren't firing before. Thinking of how serotonin works in the brain, I always thought it was produced there, but it is produced in the digestive tract, so what you eat has a big part of it.

When I decided to quit my anti-depressants and try the psychedelic route, I thought I should clean up my digestive tract so, I decided to go for two colonics. For those of you that don't know, a colonic is an enigma on steroids! They stick a tube up your rectum then shoot in and recycle about forty-five gallons of water to basically 'clean your pipes.' It washes and flushes everything out of your digestive tract and colon, which could have been hampering your digestive process and, ultimately, your serotonin production. I booked two appointments, and afterward, I felt amazing, my skin was clearer, I was happier, I wanted to go work out, exercise, and get into shape; it gave me a great outlook! I would highly recommend it to anyone as a step to help increase your mood and health.

The recipe and schedule I researched for micro-dosing called for .1 - .2 grams of mushrooms every two to three days for one month, then off for one month. When I thought about that dosage, I did the math. I'm able to buy an ounce of mushrooms illegally for one hundred and sixty dollars, that's twenty-eight grams, one hundred and sixty divided by twenty-eight is five dollars and seventy cents, break that down to .1 of a gram, is fifty-seven cents per .1 of a gram. Suppose I did .2 of a gram that would cost me one dollar and fourteen cents every two days. For the month, it would cost me seventeen dollars, as opposed to my forty-five-dollar anti-depressant prescription. If this micro-dosing works, I can see why big pharma or governments wouldn't want this secret known; anti-depressants are a nineteen billion dollar per year industry. That's a lot of profits and taxes gone if I could just grow a batch of mushrooms at home. And the quantity of mushrooms that are needed to self-medicate, .2 every other day for a month, is about three grams of mushrooms per month, which is so minimal it's astonishing.

I bought a scale, a bag of vegetarian gel caps, and a coffee grinder, a real druggie set up! Now all I needed was the mushrooms. I had researched and read a lot about mushrooms and was somewhat familiar with the different species. There are more than one hundred and eighty species of psilocybin mushrooms growing wild around the world. Some of the more familiar mushrooms include (I will use their common names instead of scientific names). Liberty Caps, Flying Saucers, Blue Runners, Blue Meanies, Philosophers Stone, Wavy Caps,

Golden Teacher, and there are Amazonian and Cambodians, just to name a few. I called my guy Al. I was referred to Al a few years back by a guy on set; Al always had whatever you were looking for, he was my guy for mushrooms, so I called him Al Zoomers. Al Zoomers always had mushrooms. All you needed to do was text him, and then a couple of hours later, he would be at your door. I asked him if he had mushrooms and what kind? He said, "of course I do, they're great, and they're blue meanies." I said, "great, see you soon?" and thirty minutes later, he was at my door with an ounce of mushrooms; Al Zoomers is the best.

When I got the ounce of mushrooms, I pulled out an equal amount of stems and caps; I wasn't following any strict protocols. I just figured if I grabbed enough of each, I should get an even amount of psilocybin, a genuinely scientific approach. I didn't know how much I needed, so I just filled the coffee grinder. I ground it for ten minutes until it was a fine powder, almost dust. I set up the scale and started to fill a gel cap, just holding it and scooping the powder with my fingers; when I weighed it, it was .4 of a gram; I was amazed because it didn't even look like a lot. I emptied half, and then I remembered that I must subtract the weight of the capsule also, I weighed an empty capsule, and it came in at .05 of a gram, so if the capsule weighed under .2 of a gram, I would be fine. When I emptied half and weighed it, it came in at .19, perfect! I weighed out ten more, and they all looked half full and came in at .18 - .19, so I just started doing them by eye; half a capsule seemed perfect. I packed fifty pills, and when I weighed them, they all came in at .17- .19; damn, I should have been a pharmacist!

When I decided to try psychedelic therapy, I learned about two schools of thought, micro-dosing and what I call mega-dosing. My game plan was to go off my anti-depressants. I would stop taking them, wait three to four weeks, then do a mega-dose, my ten-gram trip. Then, I'd wait for another three to four weeks to start a cycle of micro-dosing. The process of micro-dosing would be for approximately thirty days, one day on and one day off. With my long history of depression, addiction, and PTSD, starting with .2 of a gram, the high end of the micro-dosing amount would be better. After that micro-dosing round, I would wait another month before doing a second round; this time, I would only do .1 for a month and then assess how I was feeling. My logic for doing less was that I didn't want to build a tolerance. I wanted my mind to be fine on its own, something it has never been able to do.

When I had everything set up, I looked at the ten grams for the mega-trip, and I was a little taken aback at how many shrooms it was; I mean, it was a lot of mushrooms to eat! And, I had a lot of shrooms left over. Guess I would schedule another ten-gram trip. Once I had everything settled and figured out, I just had to sit tight until it was time for my ten-gram trip!

My Ten Gram Trip.

When the big day finally came, I was ready. I was ready, but I was also surprisingly nervous. Funny, I have done almost every drug, I have drunk myself to near alcohol poisoning, and I have done both simultaneously a lot of times. I have done acid, mushrooms, MDMA, Ecstasy, Mescaline, Cocaine, smoked Heroin, and I've drunk the real Absinthe, and here I was, nervous to eat some mushrooms. I used to do a lot of mushrooms and acid in high school, but I used them as party drugs, always smoking or drinking while doing them, but never doing them just for the therapeutic aspects. Also, seeing ten grams in the bag was a little intimidating; there was a lot more than I had expected, but I was ready.

My purpose and my intent of this trip was therapeutic. I wanted to focus on my addictions, my depression, and my PTSD. I wanted to think about my daily addiction to pot, my need to binge drink, and to think about and try to remember my car accident. Unfortunately, the details of that day were blocked. I didn't remember the facts, and I didn't know what exactly happened. I was hoping my mind would make me remember that dreaded day. To get my set and setting right, I had planned out everything. I pre-planned my entire day to ensure I was in the right frame of mind when I was ready to trip, and I had started pre-planning my playlist a couple of weeks in advance. I determined my music would be mostly instrumental; I didn't want any outside influence to steer the direction of my mind. I wanted to make sure I was alone with my thoughts, I wanted to see where my mind would go with no outside influence, and to me, that even included lyrics in my music. My entire playlist was primarily instrumental, a lot of classical, a lot of The Beatles, and a lot of Pink Floyd. As for the classical, I didn't know what I was doing, so I just downloaded all I could find. I wasn't familiar with the genre, so I just loaded up as much as I could and figured I'd just skip through what I didn't like. I went to YouTube and loaded up on Bach, Mozart, Beethoven, Chopin, Brahms, Schubert, Vivaldi, and a little Gershwin.

In the past, when I would do mushrooms, I would listen to some tunes, maybe have a drink or two, smoke a little pot, and trip out to a movie like Avatar or Alice and Wonderland. But not this time; this time would strictly be therapeutic. It would be just me and my thoughts in the dark. I only told one friend of my plan; I let him know that I would be doing a big trip, ten grams to be exact and that if I called him, I would need him to just 'talk me down.' I instructed him not to call or text, as my phone would be off, but not to freak out about that; everything would be ok; I just wanted to be alone and uninterrupted. The last thing I needed was to be deep into my trip and have my phone ring and have someone on the other end trying to trip me out, that would definitely kill my buzz, and if it happened when I was deep in my mind, that would really suck and ruin my intent.

When I woke up that day, I knew exactly what I would be doing all day, and it started with sleeping in. I got up around eleven, and the first thing I did was drink my lemon and ginger drink. An extended visit to the bathroom followed that. The night before, I had a glass of prune juice, flaxseed, Metamucil, fish, and castor oil. I wanted to make sure my system was cleansed for my trip; I wanted to make sure my body would process all the mushrooms and everything nice and easy the next day. I went to the bathroom and left with a nice big smile on my face and about ten pounds lighter, ready to tackle the day.

I had a nice relaxing day ahead of me, and I wanted to start my trip at about eight that night, which meant I wanted to eat dinner around five and digest everything by about seven. All I had to do in the day was hit the gym, do some laundry, and do some cleaning. I put on some laundry and started cooking breakfast. While I was doing that, I began to get my place ready for the night. I had to make sure my 'set and setting' was perfect, so I wanted to make sure my place was clean and comfortable. I started tidying up and blacked out my bedroom window. I had to make sure I would be in total darkness. I planned to lie in bed with just my headphones and to have it so dark that I wouldn't be able to tell the difference when my eyes were open or closed. I pulled the blinds down and hung a blackout curtain, it was perfect; not one crack of light was coming through the window.

After my breakfast, I finished my laundry and decided to head to the gym. A nice walk and work-out would get my blood flowing and give me some good energy for the evening. I had a great work-out and hit the grocery store for a salad on the way home. My plan for dinner was to eat light, so I wasn't lethargic and bogged down from a big heavy meal. It was four o'clock when I got home, so I figured I would watch a bit of TV during dinner. I wasn't going to watch anything during my trip; I would only watch something that night when I was coming down after the trip. It wasn't going to be a comedy or an animation; I was going to watch a nature documentary. I picked out "Earth at Night" on Netflix, a documentary about the nightlife of animals, all shot at night in the dark; I thought that would be a great way to end my trip.

After my dinner, I continued to putt around the apartment, getting it ready. During my investigations of tripping, I read a story of a guy, who while tripping with friends, got the urge to strip down naked, run outside and tell the world that everyone should be on mushrooms too! I wondered if something like this would happen to me, and if it did, I didn't have any friends there to stop me, so I decided I better do something to remind myself not to go out. So, I got a big thick black marker and two pieces of paper and proceeded to write, "EVERYTHING IS OK, YOU'RE ON MUSHROOMS, DON'T GO OUTSIDE!" and I signed it Myles (in case I forgot who wrote it!). Then, I taped it to the inside of my apartment door in case the urge hit me to go out!

Dinner was digesting nicely, so I decided to get my mushrooms ready for consumption. I grabbed the bag and looked at it and thought, damn, that's a lot of mushrooms! I wasn't exactly sure how I was going to eat that many, I figured I was just going to gobble them down, but I thought that might be kind of gross. I had read about 'lemon tekking.'

It's the process of grinding up the mushrooms into a powder and putting them in lemon juice. It's supposed to intensify the effects and help them hit you faster, so I decided to grind up half of them, drink those and eat the rest. I squeezed two lemons and ground five grams up in my coffee grinder; I put them in the lemon juice, which just made a thick heavy paste (this was a lot of mushrooms). I added water, stirred them up, and let them sit and soak until I was ready, and once I was ready, I would just add some more water to make the paste drinkable. I started to get everything ready. I put on sweatpants and a hoodie, I put a nice fleece blanket on the bed, and I got my iPod and earphones ready. I texted my friend and told him I was about to start and that I'd text him in the morning, I got a big thumbs up and a "best of luck" reply from him. I shut the phone off and went to the kitchen to start consuming.

The mushroom paste had become extremely thick; I added more water and a touch of pineapple juice for flavor. I stirred and stirred, then grabbed some shrooms to start eating. I proceeded to eat a mouthful, and I chewed and chewed until it became mush, and then I washed it down with the lemon mushroom slop. I repeated this five times until I finished all the dry mushrooms and all of the mushroom drink. There was some residue left in the glass, so I filled it up with water to get every speck of the mushrooms. I rinsed and rinsed my mouth to get out all the little pieces that were stuck in my teeth and swallowed them down. I sat down to digest, and I thought, wow, that was a shitload of mushrooms, this is going to be interesting.

After about ten minutes, an idea popped into my head. Someone had given me an adult coloring book for Christmas a couple of years ago, one of those therapeutic, relaxing coloring books for stress. I hadn't used it and never really thought about it until now, I figured it might be kind of cool to do while tripping, so I dug it out of my desk and grabbed the pencil crayons and put them in my bedroom for later. By now, it had been about thirty minutes, and I was starting to get the 'yawns,' so I knew they were starting to kick in, time to go into the bedroom and lie down. I went to the bedroom, pulled the curtains down tight, grabbed the headphones, and turned off the lights. I got in the bed and under the fleece blanket, and I was super comfortable. Then, I thought of what Jim Morrison said in a song, 'Is everybody in, the ceremony is about to begin.' It was time for my journey to begin.

Now, this is where time begins to fade away, I remember hearing two songs for sure, but the rest of the night just blends into itself. The first song I heard was 'Comfortably Numb' by Pink Floyd, and I took that as a sign that it would be a good night. The other song was a slow classical piece, no idea what it was, but it was perfect, a nice slow, soft string piece that put me in the ideal frame of mind for whatever was to come. As I laid in bed with my eyes closed, I remember seeing colors and patterns, my last real conscious thought was that I couldn't tell the difference when my eyes were opened and closed, but the color and patterns were still there either way.

I'm not going to explain all the little trippy things that I experienced that night, like that I tried coloring, and none of the lines would stay still, so it was super hard. I remember laughing and giggling that I was a moron for not being able to color within the lines, but honestly, it was very hard! I'm only going to talk about the three experiences that I will never forget, three events that I genuinely believe changed me and my perception forever. Two things happened that made me change my perceptions of this world and one massive event that helped me cope, deal and overcome my PTSD. I went into this night with the determination and intent to confront my addictions, depression and come to terms with my PTSD. I believe I accomplished everything.

One thing I experienced that changed my perception was just looking at a black picture frame. I have a Pearl Jam concert poster consisting of an elephant painting. The painting itself is a subliminal picture; when you look at the elephant, you can see different images within it, but this wasn't what tripped me out. The poster was in a plain black picture frame. When I was standing looking at the picture, I was drawn into the frame, which was just a black matte color on metal, but there was something that drew me in and caught my eye. As I got closer to the frame, I could start seeing colors in the black. I looked away and rubbed my eyes, then started looking closer. The closer I got, the more colors I could see, and as I stared at it, I saw a prism of light, almost like light shining through a prism and coming out different colors on the other side. I looked at every inch of that frame and saw colors throughout it. I was amazed. I thought that black contained all the colors, but after the trip, I researched and learned that black absorbs all the colors but does not reflect them to the eye. But how was I able to see the color? I looked away, I looked at other colors, but when I looked at the black, I could see all the colors of the spectrum absorbed within it. I am convinced that my mind was open and that I was, in fact, seeing things on a higher level. The following incident reinforced that with me.

As I sat on the edge of my bed with the lights on, I stared down at the floor. I had old hardwood floors that probably hadn't been refinished for years, the apartment was pretty run down, and the hardwood floors were pretty worn in spots. As I looked down at the floor, the grain in the wood started to move. I could see the lines flowing in the same direction; it was as if the grain was breathing, flowing, moving like water, each tile of wood moving in its own path and flow. It was as if the wood was alive; it made me think that this is how wood breathed when it was still a tree (I know, but bear with me), and as I looked at the different tiles, they were all flowing to their own rhythm. This was fascinating to me. I got down on my knees to get a closer look at the floor; I was hypnotized and believed that this wood was alive and felt I had to get closer. I put my face down to the floor and was only an inch away from the floor and what I saw next blew me away.

As I was looking at the grain moving, suddenly, my eyes were able to see layers to the hardwood floor. The first layer I was able to see was the finish on the wood tiles; it looked like a minuscule layer on top of the wood, almost like a sugar glaze. Below the layer of finish, I was able to see air or space between the wood itself and the finish that was once applied to it, then below that, the wood itself. I was amazed; I thought my mind was on a different level and that I could see things in this world that you can't see when your mind is closed. I mean, here I was looking at my floor and seeing the layers of molecules that made up the finish, the air between, and the wood itself. I learned that it is true what they say about this world; that everything is just matter with space between all molecules, even though it may look solid to our eyes. I was genuinely becoming enlightened, but what was to come next would truly set me free.

The primary purpose and my intent of wanting to do a mega-trip was to address the real things that were bothering me in my life. The first was my addiction, my dependence on marijuana and why it ruled me every second of every day, my binge drinking, and my use of hard drugs. The second purpose of my trip was to deal with or try to come to terms with my life-long depression and the PTSD that I suffered from my car accident fourteen years ago. Finally, I wanted to address and confront the day my life changed when my beautiful son of eight years was killed. Life hadn't been enjoyable or the same since then.

Even though I was working, supporting myself, and having a social life, everyone thought I was fine, but meanwhile, I was still hurting and suffering inside. I would think of him every day. I was consumed with PTSD and what they called 'survivors' guilt.' I was always thinking, 'why was I alive when he wasn't, I didn't deserve to be.' So, I would avoid everyday situations that reminded me of him, I'd see commercials for shows that he liked, and I would zone out and think of him, walking through stores, I would see toys and would stop to think that he probably would have loved them, it was hard to function, I couldn't even speak his name. When situations like that happened, which was every day, I would smoke and drink to numb myself down and help me forget. I would smoke every day to stop my dreams at night; I couldn't even bear to see him in my dreams. And even though I tried to confront this in my mind many times through rehab, therapy, and counseling, nothing worked. I had to confront this once and for all, and my mega-trip was the way to do it.

After my experience of seeing colors in black, the wood grain swimming and breathing, and the molecule layers, I knew my mind was on another level. I knew I was deep within myself, and I could see things and think in a way that was not visible in my normal conscious state. I believed I had penetrated and opened my third eye.

I laid in my bed and shuffled through my music until I found a slow classical song. To this day, I don't know what song it was, but it was slow and soothing, and as I listened to it, I went into a trance. It was as if I was sleeping in a heavy, deep sleep with intense dreams, but I was fully awake for them. I know I wasn't sleeping because I remember every second of it.

I was never able to remember the accident, and I was never able to see the last seconds of my sons' life. The doctors said the loss of memory could have been a result of hitting my head so hard; or that I couldn't remember it because of shock and that I was just repressing those thoughts; or what I believed to be the case, is that I fell asleep at the wheel and wasn't conscious the moment of the crash. I always took ownership for the accident, I always blamed myself for it, and I always took responsibility for it, but I could never say what exactly happened because I didn't know. I was taking him home early for a soccer tournament after he had spent the week with me. It was a two-car collision on a one-lane highway in the country on a beautiful sunny day, early on a Saturday morning. The driver of the other car and I were charged with 'crossing left of center,' which is just a traffic violation;

there were no criminal charges or dangerous driving charges involved. I know what you are wondering; you're wondering if there were drugs or alcohol involved, there wasn't. I had smoked the night before after he went to bed; the last night with him was always the hardest. Knowing that I had to take him home the next day always brought tears to my eyes and broke my heart, so I had to numb myself to get sleep. I never smoked the days I took him home. I always waited until I was back home.

The only things I remembered about the accident were packing the car in the morning and getting McDonalds before hitting the highway. Then after the accident, all I remember is waking up hanging upside down with my legs trapped between the dashboard and floor in the crumpled wreckage looking around for him. I remember seeing glass and metal everywhere and seeing the bone of my arm sticking out of my skin. I could hazily remember the helicopter that airlifted me out of there. I remember my only concern was where my son was; the attendant kept assuring me that Dalton had been taken to a different hospital and was fine. I either repressed the moments before the accident, or I honestly couldn't remember, but that was before tonight and my ten-gram trip. Tonight, I would remember the last moments before my son lost his life and when I almost died.

As I laid in my bed in a trance, I tried to focus my mind and think why I was getting high and medicating myself twenty-four hours a day, seven days a week. It made me think of all the time I had wasted in my life consumed by drugs and alcohol. After thinking that through, it led my mind to think of all the memories I had of my son and how the drugs were blocking me from remembering him, and that thought started to make me angry. The idea that something or someone (myself) wouldn't let me remember Dalton disgusted me. I was pissed off that I was stopped from thinking about that boy with such a beautiful smile that always made me smile. At that moment, I was transcended, my mind put me in the car with Dalton just moments before the accident, I felt I was physically and mentally there in that car, on that highway, in that moment of time on that bright sunny day, it was like a replay. I was behind the wheel of the car, and I heard his voice wake me up, 'Daddy, what are you doing?' I looked over my shoulder behind me and felt the car swerve, and I heard the wreckage in my head.

As soon as I heard the wreckage, I was able to hear the music again, and I was back in my bed. I said to myself for the first time, 'I fell asleep at the wheel, and he woke me up.' I always knew I was responsible, but I never knew how or why. Now I know, and now I can deal with it, I made a mistake that cost my son his life. I had to look at my phone, and though the music was still playing the whole time, I couldn't hear it, I couldn't hear anything except the thoughts in my head, the sounds from that day, and my sons' voice. I don't know how to describe my experience accurately or in a way that seems possible, but it was as if I traveled through time physically and mentally. To this day, I genuinely feel that I left that bed and was transcended back into that car on that horrible sunny day.

I sat up in my bed and turned the music off, and I cried. It was the strangest and strongest flow of emotion I have ever experienced. After my accident, I cried deep and hard for months, but this was different. It was honest. It was as if my soul was cleansing itself by weeping. Though I was on mushrooms, I felt that I was crying from my heart and in a truly honest way for the first time in my life. I felt that all my emotions before this moment were just coming from the surface and clouded. I had carried a lot of emotion about that day and about my son with me. But now, it was as if I had come to peace with all of it. Something that angered me from that day was the ambulance attendant in the helicopter. My only concern was where my son was, and that's all I kept asking; he had told me he was fine and was taken to a different hospital, I didn't know it at the time, but he was lying. Dalton died on impact. But his lying may have saved my life. If he had told me that Dalton had passed away, my will to live would have left me, he knew this, and his lying helped save my life. I never realized or thought about that until I was sitting up in my bed. Though I was sad, there was a sense of relief and happiness that I could finally think and feel honest about that day.

Even though I was probably still tripping, I felt sober. I felt like I had gone through some change. I kept the music on and sat there upright in the dark for a long while. I just sat and thought about everything. I thought about Dalton long and hard. It had been so long since I had him in my mind; it was the first time in a long time I was able to see all the good times we had together and the times he was happy. Before this moment, all my thoughts of him hurt me and were painful, it was the first time since the accident I was able to see him happy in my mind, and I didn't want it to stop. I laid back down in a very peaceful state. I don't know how long I lay there listening to music before I fell asleep. I fell asleep a new man, and I had changed my perception. I changed my thought process from negative to positive;

from being sad and grieving, to being happy and glad that I knew a child like him.

After My Ten Gram Trip.

Little did I know, the day after my ten-gram trip would be the first day of the rest of my life. I know it sounds corny and cliché, but it was the first time in my life that I would know true sobriety. It would be the first day that the fog and clouds were lifted, the first day I would ever know clarity. But the day after my ten-gram trip didn't start that way, in fact, quite the opposite. When I woke up; I was exhausted, but it wasn't a tired I had felt before. My body didn't ache; I wasn't sore or stiff; it was my mind. My head was exhausted; it felt like I worked through the theory of relativity and that I figured out the square root of every prime number between one and million, and I don't even know if those are prime numbers.

I had no idea what time I went to sleep the night before, and since I hid all my clocks before my trip, I had no idea what time it was when I woke up. I got my alarm clock out, and it said two o'clock; I wasn't sure if it was night or day until I opened my curtains and saw the daylight. It was like I was in slow motion; the simple things seemed so complicated. I wanted a bowl of cereal and a glass of orange juice, but I had to think pretty hard about how to accomplish it. I opened the cupboard and saw plates and bowls, so I just reached for a plate. I stopped to think about how to eat cereal and realized I needed a bowl, I wanted orange juice, so I had to figure out what to put orange juice in. I thought to myself, 'holy-shit, I have blown my mind!' I grabbed a mug, the milk, and orange juice, I sat down and stared at what was in front of me, but something was missing. I had to stop and think through the steps of how to get the cereal from the bowl to my mouth, 'oh ya, a spoon.' I poured the milk and orange juice; I took a spoonful of cereal and spat it out immediately. Holy shit, I poured the milk in the mug and the orange juice in the bowl. I was scared and thought I turned myself stupid, I had heard of people frying their brains, and I thought I actually did, 'oh my god, what the hell have I done to myself?' I was exhausted; I gave up eating and decided to go back to bed. I figured going back to sleep would be the safest option.

When I went back to sleep, it was about two in the afternoon. When I woke up, I looked at the clock, and it said nine o'clock, great, I slept all day, how would I ever sleep tonight. I walked out of the bedroom into the other room and saw the light outside the window; what the hell? I pulled open the curtains, and it was daylight, holy shit! I grabbed the phone and looked at the time and the date, it was nine a.m. the next day! I couldn't believe it; I slept for about seventeen hours straight through; I didn't even get up for my usual three times a night to pee! I looked around in disbelief. I sat and reflected for a second; I felt different; it was weird. I wasn't worried about sleeping that long, and I felt amazing. My mind felt crisp and awake, you know that phrase 'sharp as a tack,' I felt like that, and I have genuinely never felt like that before, ever!

I decided to go out and get a coffee instead of having another incident like the 'orange juice cereal.' When I stepped outside, things seemed different; everything looked clearer, cleaner, crisper. Trees seemed to be more defined; the leaves seemed to be more sharply outlined, more in focus, if that makes any sense. The colors were brighter; the blue sky seemed to be glowing, the clouds were the purest white I have ever seen, the grass and those trees seemed so much greener than I had ever seen them. It was so profound to me that as I walked with my coffee, I even started singing, 'I can see clearly now the rain is gone, I can see all obstacles in my way!'[27] A guy I walked by heard me and looked at me, and with a scrunched look on his face, called me a weirdo; I usually would have replied to him or let it stew in my mind for hours at what an asshole he was. Still, it didn't even phase me, hmmm.

When I got back home with the coffee, I sat and looked around; now, this is where I knew there was something different about me. I looked around and thought, 'time to do some cleaning and re-arranging.' I was a little taken aback as I dreaded cleaning, don't get me wrong, I'm not a dirty or unclean person, I'm just a little messy and unorganized, but I hate cleaning. I only clean when things get out of control, I was a 'once a month' kind of guy, but here I was excited to clean and organize my place.

---

[27] "I Can See Clearly Now," Johnny Nash 1972

As I was cleaning, I realized something significantly different about me and something entirely different in my mind. When I was in my closet, I came across the box that contained all the pictures of my son. After my accident and 'recovery,' not only was I unable to look at any pictures of my son, but I also couldn't speak his name or even talk about him. Just the thought and mention of him would send me down a dark path. I would smoke, drink, or snort anything to make me forget. It was one of the reasons I smoked so much pot; when I smoked pot, I would never dream about him, or at least I wouldn't remember it. It numbed me down so much that I wouldn't even dream of my son; it was just too hard to see him in my mind. Thinking about that would strike me with guilt and disgust that I couldn't even think of or talk about that beautiful child. He was such a cool and well-behaved child; he didn't deserve that. He deserved more than that, and he deserved to be remembered. His spirit should never have been forgotten. I should have realized and known how lucky I was ever to have a child like that in my life. But now, I decided it was time to get those pictures out and hang them. I even spoke his name out loud and said, "I am sorry, Buster (my nickname for him); I just couldn't look at these until now." I took them out of the box and stared at them; usually, I would have broken down emotionally and would have run to a bottle or a joint, but this time when I looked at them, I smiled. For the first time in fourteen years, I was able to think about my son positively, the survivors guilt seemed to be gone, and the pictures brought me comfort instead of pain. I was happy to look at my beautiful son once again.

When I finished hanging the pictures, my phone rang, I looked at the phone, and it was my mom. Now please don't judge me, but normally I would see her name on the call display, and I would have to think twice about whether to answer it or not, but not this time, I picked it up after the first ring. We didn't have the best relationship, and communication was never good between us; she was very stubborn. She prides herself on being a 'stubborn Parker', so she is not open to other peoples' feelings or needs. So, instead of communicating honestly with her, I would say just enough to avoid a fight and never really express my true feelings, as it was like pissing in the wind. But not this time, I was amazed at the conversation we had, I didn't get emotional, I didn't get worked up, and I didn't have to run and get high or have a drink afterward, oh, I should also tell you she was a massive trigger of mine! My mom was even surprised when I said hello; she replied, "oh, you picked up, oh that's a surprise." We started talking and she mentioned my brother and started to poke the beast.

Now what I mean by that is, I am estranged from my brother. A few reasons include his stealing the hockey season tickets that our family had owned for over fifty years from me, his wife, and his overall opinion of me. But the most important reason we are estranged is that he and his wife used their children as weapons, dangling them and the ability to see them over mine and my parents' heads. Now my parents being the Grand Parents, had no choice but to jump through their hoops to see the kids; I didn't, if they wanted to use their kids like that, I had no patience or respect for people like that, and I let them know. It got so bad at one point that I would just refer to their kids as the W.M.D.'s (weapons of mass destruction), as they caused so much damage in our family. Everyone understood, cousins, friends, and anyone who knew them, the only ones that couldn't admit this was my parents because if they did, they would be cut off too. I had explained this many times to my mother, but she would never take one side or another, how could she, but today when she insinuated that I should go to his place, I had to lay out the situation again, but this time I did it in a way that was calm, cool, and honest. I told her how it made me feel and how much it hurt me not to see my niece or nephew, two kids I loved and had great relationships with. This conversation was the first time that I was totally honest with my mother in a long time. I put my guard down and explained my true feelings, and I felt great. When my mom heard how this made me feel, she started to cry; she admitted that they shouldn't have done what they did but that she was powerless. I reassured her there was nothing she or I could do and that it was totally up to my brother and his wife. We had never had a conversation like this before, I always 'tiptoed' around the issues, and even though my mother cried, I felt so good that I was able to speak my mind and tell the truth finally.

After speaking with my mom, I jumped on the computer to do a little further research to see if others ever felt like this after a big psychedelic trip. I typed in 'psychedelics and PTSD,' a shitload of links came up, but one caught my eye. It was a soldier describing his PTSD and how hard life was after the war. He had lost friends and saw some horrific events that shook him to his core and shattered his view of humanity. He tried all kinds of therapy and medications upon returning from service, but nothing ever worked; he could never get out of the dark. Finally, he had decided that enough was enough and thought suicide was the only way out. As he loaded his weapon, the phone rang; it was a buddy from the service that he hadn't spoken to in years. His friend told him that he wanted to die and was in just as much pain as he was. Like him, he didn't know who to speak to; he just thought that his friend might understand what he was going through, and he did. His friend that called had heard of D.M.T. therapy that helped people with their PTSD, they both decided to take the treatment before doing anything stupid. They found a psychedelic clinic, and both went for therapy, thankfully so. The treatment was a success; they have said that they have never considered suicide since, and one of them went on to tour and give speeches and lectures to veterans suffering from PTSD and depression. Though it wasn't psilocybin, I could relate. I broke down and cried after reading that. I wasn't sure if it was from reading their touching story or from my emotion of being relieved, relieved that I finally found a way out of the darkness and depression that haunted me for years. I decided then and there that more people needed to know about this. The stigma had to be lifted about psychedelics, I was living proof that psychedelic therapy works, and I had to tell anyone that would listen.

Going forward, I would talk more openly and honestly than I had in all my life, about my feelings, about my past, about my depression, about my son, about PTSD, and about mushrooms. I wasn't afraid anymore, and I didn't need to hide my thoughts and feelings, nor would I be ashamed to tell people I did mushrooms to help with my addictions, depression, and PTSD. If the subject came up, I would discuss it with friends, family, co-workers, and anyone who wanted to talk about the topic. When I decided to put my thoughts and experiences down on paper, people would see me writing and always ask, 'what are you writing?' In that stupid mocking way, some would ask, 'what are you writing, the next great American novel?' I would look them straight in the eye and say, "No, I'm writing about a ten-gram mushroom trip I took to help me deal with my depression and addiction." I'd love to watch the expressions on their faces; no one was ever expecting to hear such an honest answer like that and especially not an answer about 'drug use' like that! From their replies, I could tell the type of person they were, 'well, that must have been one hell of a party!'. If they replied like that, usually, they were closed-minded and not open to ideas or thoughts that weren't programmed into them by society. On the other hand, the open-minded, free thinkers would be intrigued and want to discuss and discover something they knew nothing about. In other words, after this conversation, I could figure out who was cool and who wasn't.

One of the most remarkable conversations I had on the subject was when I was working on the T.V. show 'Coroner.' There was a real-life pathologist on set as a consultant. He asked what I was writing; I wasn't sure about telling him as I was nervous discussing mushrooms with such an authority figure. I answered point-blank, "I'm writing about my PTSD and a ten-gram mushroom trip I took trying to open up my third eye". He said, "Oh, your pineal gland?" I was taken aback and impressed with him right away. He proceeded to tell me about actually seeing a few pineal glands in his work when he had to dissect brains; even though it freaked me out, I was enthralled. We sat and talked for an hour, and he was a firm believer that there is more to the pineal gland than science knows. He also told me that every pineal gland he has ever seen has been calcified and said he would never drink water with fluoride again because of it (but that's a whole other book).

After my ten-gram trip, conversations with women got a lot better also. I hadn't dated for years, and it was always with the wrong types of women when I did. I dated women that deep down I knew wouldn't be with me long term. They ranged from powerful women who needed a financially successful man, and when they realized I didn't care about success or money, that would be enough for them. Then there would be sober girls who never smoked pot or drank, and when they realized they couldn't change me or get me sober, that would be it for them too. Also, there were Middle Eastern women, oh the Middle Eastern women, the Persians and Afghanis; they were my weakness; they were the women who found it taboo to date a white 'Christian/Catholic' man. They knew their family or religion wouldn't let them marry that type of guy, so they didn't stick around too long either. Suffering from PTSD, I didn't have a lot of self-esteem, and after what I had been through with my sons' mother, I was a little biased towards women. Please, don't think I was a misogynist or angry; it's just that my sense of trust was gone. I wasn't willing to let anyone into my heart or life again because that would ensure that I would never get hurt or taken advantage of again. I avoided any deep, meaningful conversations with women regarding sex, love, relationships, and feelings. But now, when I'm with friends, and in groups, I speak so honestly that I get people telling me it's such a relief to hear someone speak so honestly. I even get women that I don't know asking me out because their friends refer me; they tell them they know an honest, open man in touch with his feelings and that you should give him a call. I get friends' wives and girlfriends calling and messaging me to talk about their problems and wanting to get together for coffee, which I highly avoid.

But those aren't the main reasons I knew there had been significant changes in my brain and life. I had been up for about five hours, and I hadn't even thought about pot yet! I was a little taken aback; usually, I would hit my bong or pipe within the first fifteen minutes of waking up. Before I did my ten-gram trip, I got rid of all my pot and my paraphernalia. Bongs went in the garbage; I gave my hash pipes and glass bowls to my mailman (yes, posties love pot) and gave all my lighters to my smoking friends. But most importantly, I got rid of all the pot I had left.

Once again, I did the ceremonial, 'I'll never smoke pot again flush down the toilet.' I can't tell you how many times over the years I flushed my pot down the toilet, swearing I'd never smoke again. I probably should have given it away or sold it, but then I would have had to explain myself to someone; I thought it was better this way. When I was watching it swirl in the toilet bowl, and I wondered if I would be doing this again, I wondered if I just wasted fifty dollars, literally flushing it down the drain. When I had performed this ritual in the past, I always said to myself, "this is it; I'm never going to smoke again; I swear this is the end." But not this time; this time, I was open, hoping it would work, but I wasn't swearing it would work; it was more that I was asking this to work. I said to myself, 'I've been here before, and I don't want to be here again. I never want to have to flush pot down the toilet again.'

I was amazed that I hadn't thought of pot for a few hours. Granted, I kept my mind occupied and my hands' busy cleaning and hanging Daltons' pictures, but I didn't even want to get high after speaking with my mother! Another test would be when I didn't have anything to do. You know, the phrase 'idle hands are the devils' playground,' well, it's true. In the past, I would be able to smoke a joint and let hours fade away into nothing. I could get high and walk for an hour or sit and stare at the tv watching some mindless drivel for hours. I could watch a movie or a tv show that I had already seen ten times and still enjoy it. So today, I put on 'The Office,' a sitcom I love and that I thought I could watch over and over, but today, when I put it on, I couldn't watch it. I said to myself, 'I've seen this already, I know what's going to happen, why the hell am I watching this?' so I started cleaning again, just to stay busy.

The day after my trip, a million questions were going through my head. It was like my life was starting over again, and I had to figure out how to do things without being stoned. The real test would be when it was time to go to bed. I have been smoking myself to sleep every night for fourteen years. Would I be able to sleep? And if I was, would I dream of my son and the accident that haunted me? I decided I should go for a walk and hit the gym; if I exercised hard, maybe I would be exhausted by nightfall and just pass out. I hit the gym and used the elliptical machine for an hour; I lifted some weights and hit the sauna to start sweating out all the pot. When I got home, I was tired but not exhausted. I decided to get a pizza for dinner to celebrate and eat so much that hopefully, I would pass out from being so full. After I ate most of a large pizza, I sat around for a bit. It was about nine o'clock, and I was getting a little dozy and thought, cool, I should be able to sleep now. I went and laid down, but my head was racing; thoughts were flying through my head. I was thinking about everything, work, family, money, past, future, drugs, alcohol, and everything under the sun. I tossed and turned for about two hours with my head spinning a hundred miles an hour before I got up and realized that I wasn't going to sleep. This happened two nights in a row, not a wink of sleep in three days; it was like I was on coke again or trying to kick the oxycontin after my accident, my body had so much energy, and my mind was energized.

When I was finally able to sleep, it was a new world for me, I dreamed again, and it was as vivid and colorful as life itself. It had been over twenty years since I had a dream, and now, I could remember them. This was what my mind and soul were missing. I don't know much about dreams and the subconscious, but I genuinely believe your mind needs to be able to dream and let you see or feel things that aren't in your realm. In dreams, you can fly, you can die, you can cry, and you can relive moments from your past. The first night I slept, I experienced all those things. When I woke up, I was scared, happy, and amazed, and I could remember everything about it, it scared me a little, but it made me smile.

I was so happy that I was able to experience this again. My dream took me back to high school, and I was smoking pot; I was young, wearing my favorite jacket, and hanging with the first girl I ever loved who broke my heart. It was the weirdest dream, and I have no idea what it was trying to tell me, but it was shocking to my psyche. I was on a hill by our high school where everyone went to get high and drink; I was smoking a joint, and she was taking off her shirt! Just as she took off her bra, I was launched into the sky and started to fly, and I landed on the roof of our high school. I could still see her on the top of the hill, and as she put her shirt back on, I jumped off the roof and fell straight to the ground, and landed on my face, and that's when I woke up. I had no idea why I would dream something like that, but it was great to see my first girlfriend with her top off again! And ever since I quit smoking pot, I dream every night. Sometimes, I can be dreaming, and I wake up to go the bathroom, then when I fall back asleep, I can fall right back into the same dream; it's incredible. But the most amazing thing is that I dream of my son again. Sometimes they are happy dreams; sometimes they make me sad, but no matter what the dream, I'm just happy to see my son again.

After my ten-gram trip, there were a few setbacks, one of the setbacks was my diet. It was weird; usually, people associate smoking pot with getting the munchies and eating a ton of junk food. I was the opposite. When I was smoking pot, people were amazed when they saw my diet. Even though I would put copious amounts of smoke into my body, drown my liver in alcohol, and take any poison put in front of my face, I was conscientious and picky about my diet. I wasn't vegan or a vegetarian; I would just stay away from fast food and processed foods. If I had a choice between a burger and fries or a salad, I would go for the salad. I would read food labels, and I would stay away from M.S.G. So, when I quit smoking pot and drinking, I never would have thought that my diet would change. When I was sober, it was weird that I started eating like a fat kid at a carnival. I wouldn't care what I ate; the greasier, the better, the sweeter, the better, and the more of it, even better! Combine this shitty diet with a lack of motivation at the gym; I started gaining weight. People were a little surprised at my weight gain, and so was I.

The most notable change and setback with getting sober was my focus. The first couple of months of being sober, it was almost impossible to stay focused on anything longer than five minutes. I would try to read books, get bored and just put them down after a few pages. I would watch movies and T.V. shows for a few minutes and then just change the channel; it was tough to focus on anything. I would read news or magazines articles, and I couldn't even finish them. I would read three-quarters of the article or to the last paragraph and then just stop. I didn't have the focus or the interest in finishing it; it was alarming.

My mind was constantly racing, almost spinning, and I just couldn't focus. In conversations with people, I would start to drift away from whatever they were saying as I stood there in front of them. People would then ask me a question about what we were just talking about or ask my opinion, and I would have no idea what was just said or what they were talking about; it made for some awkward moments. It also became an issue at work. As an actor, you must take your cues from the dialogue that was being said, and sometimes as the dialogue was being spoken, I would forget and almost start drifting away. These scenes were just thirty seconds to a minute long, and I couldn't even follow along. It was getting bad. My focus and interest in exercise were also gone. Before I was sober, I would smoke a joint when going to the gym or before I went for a bike ride or rollerblading. I would be able to stay at the activity for as long as needed; now, I couldn't, I would lose interest, and my focus would be non-existent. I just couldn't stay focused.

I realized that maybe this is one of the reasons why I was self-medicating most of my life. My thoughts moved fast, and my mind was hyperactive. From a young age, I could think through twenty ideas while most people were still on their first. I had more energy and more passion than most people I knew. It was also one of the reasons I was successful in my jobs. I would play 'devil's advocate' when brainstorming new ideas as I could think through different scenarios while most people at the table were only thinking through the original idea. Though it served me well at work, it was a hindrance and troubling in my personal life. For instance, if there was a new girl in my life, I would think through the different scenarios of where we could end up, and most didn't like that, they would say I could never live in the moment, I was always thinking how things could be different or what would happen to us down the road. I also realized that this is why I might be eating so much.

Before, I would use drugs and alcohol to control my emotions. If I got upset or frustrated with something, I could always run to pot to calm myself down; it was a way of escaping situations and moments where I wasn't comfortable. If I knew I was putting myself into a stressful situation, say, dinner with the parents, seeing my ex, or going out on dates, I could numb down so my emotions would be in check. I knew I wouldn't fly off the handle or get too deep in any given situation. If I was too stoned or drunk, I wouldn't give-a-fuck. But now, I was using food to escape and using food to settle my emotions. If I was bored, I would eat; if I was nervous, I would eat; if I was scared, I would eat; and if I was upset, I would eat. Now I truly understood binge eating and why people would talk about eating a tub of ice cream to feel better.

But the most convincing thing that has happened since my trip, and it confirms that there has been a change in my brain, is that I don't get high every day anymore or drink myself numb. I don't even think about it anymore. While before, my mind would be consumed with thoughts of, 'when am I going to get high again?'. If I only had two or three grams of weed left when I was smoking, I would consider that being out, and I would need to pick up before I was completely out. Only having two or three grams would be considered 'Defcon Two,' and if I was out of pot, that would be 'Defcon One,' which would mean Myles will go to war to find pot. In my entire life, I was only at 'Defcon One' twice, and when I was at that level, I just drank myself numb. I'm so glad you can get alcohol everywhere and anytime (sarcastic tone).

So much of my time, energy, and money was consumed all my life, making sure I had pot or knew where to get it. If I went on vacation, the first thing I had to do was score some pot. It was so bad that I remember a few times when I had to be creative with acquiring or making sure I had pot. I remember one time when going to the Dominican Republic for a wedding. I was concerned about how I would get pot, so before I left, I made a batch of pot cookies. It was a lot easier to get edibles through customs than trying to get actual weed through. Another time, when I had to train at the Hard Rock Cafe in Niagara Falls, NY for three months, I walked through the restaurant on the first day asking everyone, 'hey, do you know where I can find some pot?' the kitchen guys hooked me up, I should have started with them, kitchen guys always have pot! Another time, I remember when I was working on the road in retail setting up the party stores, I was stuck away from home longer than expected, and I was running low, 'Defcon Three' levels. I knew the secretary of the President at head office smoked, so I arranged with her to 'fed ex' me half an ounce and ship it through the company account to the address of the store I was setting up; yup, I would do anything to make sure I had something to smoke. I even had to 'hoop' some at one point. What is 'hoop,' you may ask? Well, when I was going to Las Vegas for a wedding, I stuck five grams of hash up my ass to smuggle through customs when flying down. Hence, the term 'hoop.' Yup, I would do anything.

But not now; now it's a new world. I don't think about getting high anymore at all. It doesn't consume me, and it's not my priority. The energy, the money, I wasted on pot, is a thing of the past. I can sit anywhere with anyone and enjoy the time. I can enjoy the moment I'm in. My mind is present and not wandering, thinking about my next toke or when and where am I'm going to get more pot.

I want to say that I haven't smoked anything in a year, but if I did, I would be lying to you. I bought pot once, about six months after my trip. Old habits are hard to break, and that was the problem. I didn't smoke because I was hurting; I didn't smoke because I wanted to numb myself down; I didn't smoke because of friends or at a party; I smoked because of boredom. I was out for a long walk, and I'm not making excuses, but now that pot is legal, I'd smell it on every block, and I'd walk by a half dozen pot shops in ten minutes. I figured it wouldn't hurt, but it did. I used to get such pleasure and relaxation from smoking, but not this time. I was riddled with paranoia and overwhelmed with guilt. I felt I let myself down and that I was doing something wrong, and I was, I was doing something that my mind didn't need or want anymore. After that one, 'relapse,' I knew I had to change my behavior. I knew my mind had changed, but I had to make sure I changed my habits and how I spent my time. I read all the time now, I have developed an exercise routine that I stick to, and I'm dating now. I spend my time meeting new people and learning new things. It took a while but, but I know now, I will never smoke again.

But since my mushroom therapy, I'm not dependent on anything. My mind doesn't run to pot anymore, and alcohol is a social entity. Besides my relapse with pot, I have gotten drunk once. I had some beers with a few friends, but I didn't go overboard; I cut myself off after a few because I didn't feel the enjoyment I used to from drinking. When my friends brought the shots out, I passed. I didn't feel the need to get drunk as I did in the past. After the ten-gram trip, I have no urge to drink again.

Since my trip, my mind has been open to thoughts and ideas it never was before. I watch movies and listen to music that I would never have been interested in, in the past. I don't fight with people over their positions or views, and I have stopped judging or arguing when we have differing opinions. I have done a couple of trips since my big ten-gram trip and have micro-dosed for a couple of rounds, and every time I do, it brings me one step closer to opening my third eye wider.

I'm able to see outside the box. I never really knew what that meant because I didn't know what the box was. The box is our minds. We all live trapped in our beliefs. We think we know what the truth is, and it's not until you can open and free your mind that you can accept, understand, and digest things that are bigger than ourselves. The mushroom took me there, and I know it will take me further. Alcohol, anti-depressants, opioids, junk/fast food and marijuana all seemed to keep me from moving my mind and soul forward. Yes, they changed my mood, but they never changed my conscience, but the mushroom did. It freed me.

Mushroom Entertainment
Set, Setting, and Intent

There are many different factors that influence whether you will have a good trip or not, they can be summarized by one simple phrase, 'Set and Setting', and if you go a little further you can add 'Intent'. Set and Setting is a phrase coined by Timothy Leary in the early days of psychedelics. 'Set' refers to the internal, your state of mind, your mood, or your mindset, and 'Setting' refers to your external environment, where you are; what you are doing; and who you are with. Intent is summarized as, 'What is the intention of your trip, a fun party night with friends, a casual evening in the outdoors, or a therapy session to look deep within yourself?'

People have many different opinions on what to do, where to go, what to watch or what to listen to while tripping, but it really comes down to the purpose (intent) of your trip. You could be tripping for recreational fun by yourself or with others, or you could be tripping for therapeutic purposes. The best advice I can give, is that if you aren't in the right 'mindset', if you are in a bad mood or if something is bugging you, DON'T TRIP. Postpone it and save it for another time, the most important thing is to be in a good headspace when you are going to trip. After set, it's the 'setting', make sure you have the right setting and that you are comfortable. If you had plans to trip at a friends' place or out in a park and your plans suddenly change to going to a club or bar, don't think that you should still trip. Where you are and what you are doing are just as important as your 'set'. Again, my most important advice is to make sure you are happy and comfortable no matter what type of trip you are taking. Always try to get your head in the right mind space before tripping. On the day of your trip, make sure to eat right and try to get some exercise, a healthy body and healthy mind will make for a good trip, if you aren't feeling it, DON'T TRIP!

If you are tripping for recreational purposes, there are many different activities that might entertain you. The first choice for me is being outdoors, sitting and chilling in nature is awesome and sitting near a fire or water is even better, there is something very relaxing and hypnotizing watching and listening to waves or watching and listening to a fire dancing and crackling. You could go for a nature hike, but I wouldn't recommend it, getting strenuous exercise while tripping is never good. If you are with a group, it is great to just sit, talk, listen to music, and laugh outside.

If movies are your thing, it can be fun to sit and watch some movies, but it can also be scary as hell, so be careful of what you decide to watch. If you're watching with a group of people, make sure you all decide on what to watch so everyone has a good trip. It's not the time to get your buddies to watch Friday the Thirteenth or a slasher film when you are tripping. Make sure everyone agrees on what to watch.

If you are sitting around listening to music it's the same thing, make sure you are all in agreement on what to and what not to listen to. One time when I was tripping with a friend, he put some Eagles on and it utterly ruined my trip. Just like 'The Dude', 'I fucking hate the eagles man!'. Music is very important, it can really make or break your vibe, so make sure everyone agrees on the music. If chilling inside you might consider getting some color changing light bulbs. There has been some remarkable progress in psychedelic lighting since the lava lamp days of the sixties and seventies. One of the best investments I made was a WIFI 'smart control' color changing bulb, it can be controlled through an app on your phone, it really adds to the trip when just hanging in and listening to music.

Another great thing to do while tripping, either if you are doing it for recreation or therapy, alone or with a group, is to view art. And just like the advancements of lighting, psychedelic artwork has evolved since the black light velvet posters of the sixties and seventies. One thing that is great to do is to create a slide show on your TV or computer of some funky trippy or artwork. These can be pictures of anything, including nature landscapes, drawings, computer animation and even movie stills. Used in combination with music and lighting, this can be an awesome psychedelic experience. I once stared at drawing by Mario Martinez for two hours, the more I starred at it, the more images I kept discovering, it was amazing. There are also many new interactive trippy websites that have been created in the last few years. These include websites for making music, drawing, or just watching psychedelic visuals move across the screen.

If you are tripping with that special someone, having a romantic psychedelic evening for two, your music, movies, and mood choices maybe different than when chilling with friends, but the same rules apply, just agree on all choices. If choosing mood lighting, make sure you agree whether it be strobe lighting, black lights, color changing lights or candles. Strobe lights can be a little too much for some people and if using candles, practice extreme caution and it might be a good idea to have an extinguisher nearby.

If you are going to movies or clubs or bars, be careful. I'm always very hesitant about being out in public when tripping. Being around people that aren't tripping can make you very self-conscious and ruin your buzz. You're always wondering what people are thinking about you and wondering if they know you are on drugs. I remember one horrible trip when I went and saw 'Alice in Wonderland' in a theatre, I hadn't done mushrooms in over a decade. First, we had to take public transportation, which was horrible and when we arrived at the theatre it got worse. The theatre was packed, there were people everywhere, when me and my buddies were walking through the theatre and laughing, people would be turning heads and staring. When we picked our seats, the theatre was relatively empty, but the closer it got to the movie starting the more crowded the theatre got and soon the theatre was full. Looking around and seeing everyone in there, I started to get really freaked out, it was so crowded I felt everyone was staring and talking about us, I thought the whole theatre knew we were tripping so I had to get the hell out of there. We were sitting in the middle of the theatre and trying to get out of the row was a horrific experience, asking everyone to 'excuse me, pardon me, excuse me', scared the hell out of me, I thought everyone knew I was tripping so I just started saying, 'I'm on mushrooms, 'scuse me, I'm on mushrooms, pardon me, I have to get the hell out of here, pardon me'. Apparently, I said it so loud and in such a panic, that the whole theatre heard me, and it broke out in laughter. The laughter settled me down and made me laugh but I had to get the hell out of there anyway. The moral of that story is to be in total control of your set and setting. Outside influences can ruin your trip and scare the hell out of you.

Since everyone has different tastes and preferences, there are many tv, music and art genres that you may enjoy while tripping and there are many you might not like tripping too. For me, I enjoy alternative, heavy metal and rap music, but while I'm tripping I don't. The fast pace and fast lyrics make my head spin while I'm tripping, so I avoid them. It's not necessarily your favorites that you will listen to while tripping. Pearl Jam is my absolute favorite band in the world, but I will never listen to them when I'm tripping, it's kind of weird. And in contrast, I normally don't listen to Pink Floyd when I'm straight, it's not my daily 'go to', but, when I trip, it's my first choice. Same with classical music, I'll never listen to it while chilling out on a normal day, but when I eat mushrooms, it's one of my favorite genres, it's weird. Movie wise, I love thrillers, dramas, and documentaries, but not while tripping, I only watch comedies and animation movies with nature documentaries being the exception. I love stupid funny movies when I'm on mushrooms, I recently watched the animation comedy 'Sausage Party' and I loved it, on a normal day, I would never consider watching.

I also enjoy kid animation movies while tripping, Bugs Life, Toy Story and Shrek are some of my favorites, so you can see I like to keep it light and funny while tripping.

Below, I have included lists of music, movies, art, and websites that I have tripped out to or that friends have referred to me and are of the psychedelic genre. You may recognize some, and some that might be new to you, you may like some and you may hate some, either way, follow your gut and trip out to whatever makes you happy and smile.

Music To Trip To:

These are just a sampling, you can see my tastes are from the classic rock genre, and in my opinion, most great psychedelic albums were made in the heyday of the psychedelic sixties and seventies.

The Beatles – Sgt. Peppers Lonely Hearts Club Band, Rubber Soul, Magical Mystery Tour, Revolver

The Beach Boys – Pet Sounds, Surf Sounds, Wild Honey

Pink Floyd – Dark Side of the Moon, but also EVERY ALBUM

The Doors – Strange Days, The Doors, Waiting for the Sun, EVERY ALBUM

The Jimi Hendrix Experience – Electric Ladyland, Are You Experienced

Prince – Sign O' The Times

Syd Barret – The Madcap Laughs (not recommended for first trip! Barret

Black Sabbath – Black Sabbath

The 13ᵗʰ Floor Elevators – The Psychedelic Sounds of the 13ᵗʰ Floor Elevators, Easter Everywhere

The Orb – The Orb's Adventures Beyond the Ultraworld

Frank Zappa – Hot Rats

Genesis – Foxtrot

Silver Apples – Silver Apples

DJ Shadow – Endtroducing

King Crimson – In the Court of Crimson King

Velvet Underground – Velvet Underground & Nico

PM Dawn – Of the Heart of The Soul and of the Cross, The Utopian Experience

Country Joe & The Fish – Electric Music for The Mind & Body, I Feel Like I'm Fixin' to Die

Jefferson Airplane – After Bathing at Baxters, Surrealistic Pillow

Kaleidoscope – Beacon from Mars

Spirit – Spirit

The Byrds – Fifth Dimension

Love – DeCapo, Forever Changes, Love

The Moody Blues – In Search of the Lost Chord

Eric Burden and The Animals – The Twain Shall Meet

Quicksilver Messenger Service – Quicksilver Messenger Service, Happy Trails

Donavan – Sunshine Superman

The Rolling Stones – Their Satanic Majesties Request

Nirvana – The Story of Simon Simopath

The Dream Syndicate – The Universe Inside

The Dukes of Statosphear – 25 O'clock

Funkadelice – Maggot Brain, Free Your Mind and Your Ass Will Follow, Funkadelic

Curtis Mayfield – Superfly

The Who – The Who Sell Out

The Incredible String Band – The 5000 Spirits or the Layers of the Onion

Kaleidoscope – A Beacon from Mars.

Movies to Watch When Tripping:

You will see from my list below, that I like to keep my visuals 'light' and funny while tripping. For example, I love all the kid animation movies, they trip me out so much and make me laugh so much, some of the characters and animation blow my mind! Even though I will listen to Pink Floyd while tripping, and even though I like watching their movie 'The Wall', I will never watch it while tripping, I find it too heavy and dark to watch when I'm on mushrooms. You might be into horror movies and love being scared while tripping, I certainly don't and I don't recommend it, but to each their own! You might laugh at some of my selections, and you may think some of my choices are childish and dumb, but when I'm tripping, I love to see bright colors, funny drawings, a living Mr. Potato Head, talking fish or a talking donkey, come on folks, a talking donkey can be funny.

Movies and TV Shows:

Beetlejuice, Avatar, Fear and Loathing In Las Vegas, Alice In Wonderland (2010), The Big Lebowski, Time Bandits, Brazil,

Inception, The Matrix, Monsters Inc, Monster University, Fantasia, Despicable Me, Interstellar, 2001: A Space Odyssey, Corpse Bride, The Nightmare Before Christmas, Earth at Night, Yellow Submarine, Head, Rocky Horror Picture Show, Shrek, Labyrinth, Lego Movie, Finding Nemo, Fantastic Planet, Tenacious D 'The Pick of Destiny', Dr. Strange, Willy Wonka and the Chocolate Factory, The Wizard of Oz, Guardians of the Galaxy, Avengers, Xmen, Tron, Howl's Moving Castle, Who Framed Roger Rabbit, Alice Through the Looking Glass, Donnie Darko, The Dark Crystal, Enter the Void, A Scanner Darkly, Wreck It Ralph, Sin City, Eternal Sunshine of the Spotless Mind, Star Wars, The Hitchhikers Guide To The Galaxy, Rick and Morty, The Midnight Gospel, Adventure Time, Cosmos, Donnie Darko, Ren and Stimpy, Blade Runner, Planet Earth and any David Attenborough nature movie.

Psychedelic Artwork:

There are many different psychedelic artists and themes, some can be religious, humorous, space based, nature based, practical photographs or SPFX pictures. You can trip to Surrealism, Cubism, Modern, sculptures or anything you want. It just depends on what stimulates your mind and keeps you entertained. The following are a list of artists and some of their illustrations, paintings, or images that I have stared at for hours!

Salvador Dali (The King of Trippy)

- The Disintegration of the Persistence of Memory (1954)
- The Persistence of Memory (1931
- Apparition of Face and Fruit Dish on a Beach (1938)

- Geopoliticus Child Watching the Birth of New Man (1943)
- Melting Watch (1954)

M.C. Escher

-Relativity (1953)   - Stars (1948)

-Sky and Water I (1938)   -   Convex   and   Concave
(1955)

-Hand with Reflecting Sphere (1935). -House of Stairs (1951)

-Print Gallery (1956)   -Bond of Union (1956)

David Normal

- The Lord of Misrule   -The Pool
- Curioscillotropy   -Chemical Imbalance
- The Human Tree

Mario Martinez

- Mars I Afterthought   -Mars   I   Ultraviolet
  Dreams
- Mars I World Within Worlds

Some other artists that are very entertaining:

Pablo Amaringo, Ted Wallace, Dennis Konstantin.

Trippy Websites:

Technology has really advanced the ability of psychedelic art and visuals. The following websites are so visually stimulating you will find yourself laughing, saying 'whoooaaaaa', and 'cooooooool' so much that hours will slip away watching or interacting w, you'll even get goosebumps from a lot of it. If you can hook your computer to a big screen, do it, you won't be disappointed.

Falling Falling – www.fallingfalling.com A never-ending cascade of colors that fall from above and hypnotize

ZoomQuilt – www.zoomquilt.org A never ending loop of seamless images that keep going and going and going…

Arcadia Zoomquilt. www.arkadia.xyz - Same as arcadia but with more monsters and flora that keep going and going…

Audiograph – www.audiograph.xyz – A visualization to Pilotpreists 2016 album.

WikiGalaxy – www.wiki.polyfra.me – A 3D web experiment that takes the knowledge of the world and displays it visually.

Earth Nullschool www.earth.nullschool.net –Real-time data and visual of global wind patterns, temperature, and currents

Canopy – www.onecm.com/projects/canopy/ - Just click and start falling, all I can say.

Weavesilk – www.weavesilk.com – Just click and start drawing, that's all I can say.

Turing Fluid Simulator – www.webglplayground.net/new Click, drag, and trip!

A Virtual Planetarium – www.cosmic-symbolism.com Trippy cosmic pictures you can control going into.

Barry Martin's Hoplaong Orbits Visualizer – www.iacopoapps.appspot.com Fast trippy images, hold on!

OMFGDogs – www.omfgdogs.com An old school visual of dogs and colors, you can probably only watch for 1 minute.

Patatap – www.patatap.com – A music and visual creating app.

Neave.tv - www.neave.tv – Approach with caution, flipping through TV channels and you just never know what you might see. Remember, I said approach with caution.

In Conclusion:

Where do I begin to summarize the most important realizations I've ever had in my life? We never know where our lives are going, and they can change 'on a dime,' for better or worst. On the day of my accident, on that dreaded highway, my life changed for the worst. And it changed for the better during a casual 'off the cuff' conversation about micro-dosing. Even though we think we have a plan, we truly never know where life will take us.

When I started to research psychedelic therapy, mega and micro-dosing, I thought I would read a few books, watch a couple of YouTube videos, and be done with it. I never imagined I would spend a year and a half consuming everything I could about psychedelics. I never thought I would become an investor in psychedelic stocks, never imagined that I would start growing mushrooms, and I never imagined I would want to write a book and tell the world. But the more I read, the deeper I had to go. I have always questioned authority. Ever since grade nine, when I learned about the false flag event of the 'Gulf of Tonkin,' I never really trusted our government. And the more I read about psychedelics and their history with the medical community and the government, the deeper and deeper I had to go, and I am glad I did.

Not only was I able to open my' third eye' with psilocybin mushrooms, but they also opened my eyes to the world we live in and made me realize everything isn't really as it seems or how it is presented to us. There is always a 'motivation' to any messages we receive, and most times, that motivation is money, power, or control. Learning about how the government banned the use of psychedelics regardless of their therapeutic benefits made me realize that they can lie about anything that can benefit the masses. Whether it be about nutritional, financial, or spiritual information, the government will keep the truth from us if it serves them. And unfortunately, our governments have been hijacked by corporate interests. Financial regulators in the SEC are from wall street; FDA representatives are from big pharma; EPA regulators are from big oil, coal, and chemical companies; and the FCC is full of former big tech executives. These people serve their former employers and not the people. A handful of entities owns our media outlets and entertainment providers, and those entities have interests in all other facets of industry. If a product is poisoning us, outlets won't report it, and we will never hear about it because their owners have a financial interest in that product. Corporations and the dollar hijacked our truth and reality, and I learned that through mushrooms. Lobbyists represent all facets of industry, though some do act 'for the good' of the people representing charities and environmentalists. The majority of lobbyists act as representatives for big businesses. This includes big oil, pharma, big tobacco, the fast-food industry, gun manufacturers, plastic, chemical industries, etc. They are the intermediate for money to be exchanged between corporations and politicians. As of 2019, there were eleven thousand eight hundred and ninety-four registered lobbyists in the United States[28]; as of the same time, there were five hundred and thirty-five members of Congress in the Senate and Congress, that's twenty-two lobbyists for every politician. If that doesn't prove to you that something is wrong with our system and that's it's been hijacked by corporate America, I don't know what will.

It's this same system that has kept the benefits of psychedelic therapy from the people. The war on drugs is big, big money. From enforcement to incarceration, you are talking billions and billions of dollars, couple that with the anti-depressant industry, you are talking about trillions of dollars. Do you think that the companies that control these industries would just let legalization happen? Do you think they would just let their cash cow slip away and lose profits? Not a chance, and therefore, psychedelics have been demonized in our society for that very fact. But the funny thing is, if I didn't start reading, researching, and educating myself with information and connecting many dots, I would never have learned any of this. I would have just had my original, ignorant ideas (just like most of the population) that psychedelics are horrible, monstrous drugs with no purpose, when in fact, the **EXACT** opposite is the actual reality.

This discovery about corporations and government showed me what people are capable of, and it woke me up to the reality of this world. My psychedelic therapy allowed my mind to deal with and come

---

[28] Number of lobbyists in U.S 2000-202 Statista.com, March 2021

to terms with this new reality. After my micro and mega-dosing, I reprogrammed to digest and think through anything I learned in this world; it is as if it slowed my thinking and slowed my reactionary process. No longer would I jump to conclusions or assume that I knew anything until I thought the situation out through and through. I had no preconceived ideas after this journey. I believe nothing, and it serves me well.

I lived my entire life with addiction and depression, and I assumed that I always would. I never was able to shake it, but now my mind knows that's not the case, and as I said, I don't assume anything now. I would have never guessed that I would be able to free my mind and soul with psychedelics, let alone any other recourse. It would be best to lose your preconceptions to find what is real in this world, we have all been conformed one way or another, and it is time to find your freedom. I thought I was trapped; I thought I would never be able to break free from the cloud of depression and PTSD that haunted me. I never knew if I would find relief, and I never knew where I would find that relief, but I never stopped looking. I gave every avenue a try, I never gave up hope, and I kept searching, and I hope you keep searching for your relief.

After my ten-gram trip, I started to follow the money regarding psychedelic therapy. You know that old expression 'follow the money?'. When you want to get to the bottom of a conspiracy or solve a crime, they say to 'follow the money,' well, I decided to do that. I started looking into stocks and companies that were beginning to go down the psychedelic therapy route. I discovered many start-up companies, but I also found a lot of publicly traded (big pharma) companies were starting to invest in this 'new' avenue. They included Johnson and Johnson; a company that had been sued because their baby talcum powder caused cancer (which they knew). They were also sued for their involvement in the opioid crisis; if these guys were getting in on psychedelics, I knew there was something there. As of the date of publishing, psychedelic research and stocks are starting to soar. Canada recently allowed a few palliative patients on their way out of this life to consume psilocybin to help them cope with their fears of dying. The Canadian government has also recently prescribed a few doctors the right to consume psychedelics, so they know what they will be prescribing to their patients. Canada is on the cusp of legalizing psychedelics, and a handful of states have decriminalized psychedelics, including Oregon, Texas, Massachusetts, Michigan, and Washington DC.

But now that I have learned how to rethink this world and rethink my being, I'm free. I now understand movie characters like 'The Dude' in 'The Big Lebowski.' If you want to walk around in a bathrobe, if you want to wear socks with sandals if you want to wear white after Labor Day, do it. Do whatever makes you happy within yourself; that's what this life is all about. I lived my life chasing money and trying to do what society and everybody told me to do, but what I have learned, society and everyone was just telling me what 'they' wanted from me in this life, they weren't concerned with my happiness, only how my life made their existence feel. Live for yourself, live for your gut instinct and live for your heart. If people can't accept that, then they aren't meant to be on your path. Unfortunately, some of those people might be your parents, they might be your brothers or sisters, and they might be what we consider 'friends' at the time. But when the lights go out, and it is just you and your mind; it is just you and your mind, everyone else will be considering their 'being' before thinking about yours. Mushrooms not only freed me from my addictions, depressions, and PTSD, but they also freed me from society's preconceptions, in laymen's terms, 'I lightened up' and don't take myself too seriously. If everyone could experience their ego dying, this would be a much better world, and we would all be able to get along.

Thank you for sticking around and making it this far; I hope you learned a bit about psilocybin mushrooms and how psychedelic therapy might be able to help you. If I do have to summarize, all I can say is mushrooms got me sober, they stopped me from craving alcohol and pot, and they helped me deal and live with my PTSD. They have helped me enjoy life again, allowing me to live a better and more full life. They opened my mind, and this allowed me to open my heart.

Please, if you think you have run out of options, if you believe there is no way out of the darkness, please seek medical help. If you feel psychedelic therapy might be for you, try to find a psychedelic clinic near you, reach out and ask for help. If psychedelics could help someone as bad as me, they can probably help someone like you too.

Peace and Love
Myles.

Thank you for reading through my story. If you would like to comment or send a message, I would love to hear what your thoughts are. And if you have the time, if you can leave a review on amazon, it will help spread the word and would be much appreciated, thank you.

Mylesbradley21@gmail.com

Resources:

Psychedelic Clinics:

Field Trip Health – Los Angeles, New York, Chicago, Houston, Atlanta, Amsterdam, and Toront 1-888-519-519-6016

Wholeness Center – Fort Collins, Colorado - 970-221-1106

Craig Salerno Counseling – Boulder, Colorado – 973-818-7793

Marcela Ot'alora G – Boulder, Colorado - 303-818-1419

Ember Health - New York, NY – 347-547-3258

Will Siu – Los Angeles, California -

Synthesis – Amsterdam, Netherlands

California Center for Psychedelic Therapy – Los Angeles, California – 213-608-0121

Mindbloom Center – New York, NY – 929-274-0518

John Hopkins Center for Psychedelic and Conscious Research – Baltimore, MD 410-550-2253

Institute for Integrative Therapies – St. Paul, Minn. – 651-307-5148

Mindcure – Vancouver, BC – 888-593-8995

Ballard Psychiatry – Seattle, WA – 206-452-6009

SILO Wellness – Springfield, OR – 541-525-9190

Trip Sitter Corp – Austin TX

Numinus Wellness Inc – Vancouver, BC – 833-686-4687

Thrive Counselling Clinic – Vancouver, BC – 604-227-0297

Websites:

M.A.P.S. – Multidisciplinary Association for Psychedelic Studies – 831-429-6370 - www.maps.org

Michael Pollan – MY HERO, MY INSPIRATION. Psychedelic Truthsayer www.michaelpollan.com

Psychedelic Support - www.psychedelic.support

Psychedelic Assisted Psychotherapy - www.mindspacewellbeing.com

Center for Psychedelic & Consciousness Research – www.hopkinspsychedelic.org

Mind Medicine Australia – www.mindmedicineaustralia.org.au

American Psychiatric Association - www.psychiatry.org/patients-families/ptsd

Field Trip Health Assisted Therapy – www.fieldtriphealth.com

Psychedelic Psychotherapy Forum – www.psychedelicpsychotherapy.ca

Katyasivak Counselling – www.katyasivak.ca

Psychedelic Stocks

(Don't miss the incoming 'Shroom Boom, this is not financial advice)

RVVCN RVVTF – Revive Therapeutics

FTRPF – Field Trip Health

MCUR.CN – Mind Cure Health Inc

PULL.CN – Pure Extracts Technology

SHRMF – Braxia Scientific Corp.

MYCOF – Mydecine Innovations

TRIP.CN – Red Light Holland

ATAI – Atai Life Science N.V.

MMED.NE – Mind Medicine

CMPS – Compass Pathways

HAVN - Haven Life Sciences

CLXPF - Cybin

SELOS - Seelos Therapeutics

LOBE - Lobe Sciences

PHRM - PharmaTher

HOLL - Hollister Biosciences

SILO - Silo Wellness

NUMI - Numinous Wellness

EHVVF - Ehave Inc

MSET - Mindset Pharma

NEON - Neonmind Biosciences

PSYB - PsyBio Therapeutics

TRYP - Tryp Therapeutics

PSYK.NE - Horizons Psychedelic ETF

References:

LSD, Spiritually, And the Creative Process
Marlene Dobkin de Rios, 2003 Park Street Press isbn:0892819731

Frontiers of Psychedelic Consciousness. Conversations with Hoffman, Grof, Strassman and others.
David Jay Brown, 2015 isbn:1620553929

How To Change Your Mind: What the New Science of Psychedelics Teaches Us About Consciousness, Dying, Addiction, Depression and Transcendence.
Michael Pollan 2018 isbn:1594204225

Drugs As Weapons Against Us: The CIA's Murderous Targeting of SDS, Panthers, Hendrix, Lennon, Cobain, Tupac and Other Activists
John Potash, 2015 isbn:1937584924

The Use of LSD in Psychotherapy and Alcoholism
Harold Alexander Abramson, Bobbs-Merril Publishing 1967 isbn:1159088

Poisoner In Chief: Sidney Gottleib and the CIA Search for Mind Control
Stephen Kinzer, 2019 isbn:1250140439

In Search of the Magic Mushroom: A Journey Through Mexico
Jeremy Stanford, 1973 isbn:0517501546

Acid Test: LSD, Ecstasy, and the Power to Heal
Tom Shroder, 2014 Penguin Group isbn:97803999162794

Advances in Psychedelic Medicine State-Of-The-Art Therapeutic Applications
Ben Sessa, 2019 isbn:1440864101

Psilocybin Mushrooms of the World: An Identification Guide
Paul Stamets, 2019 isbn:0898158397

Fantastic Fungi – How Mushrooms Can Heal, Shift Consciousness, and Save the Planet
Paul Stamets, 2019 isbn:1683837045

Psychedelic Medicine: The Healing Powers of LSD, MDMA, Psilocybin and Ayahuasca.
Richard Louis Miller, 2017 Park St Press, isbn:1620556979

Sacred Mushroom of Visions: Tonanacatl: a source book on the Psilocybin Mushroom
Diane Darling, Ralph Metzner. 2006 isbn:1594770441

Trip: Psychedelics, Alienation and Change
Tao Lin, 2018, isbn:1101974516

True Hallucinations: Being an Account of the Author's Extraordinary Adventures In The Devil's Paradise
Terrence McKenna 1993, isbn:0062505459

LSD, My Problem Child: Insights and Outlooks
Albert Hoffman, 2013 isbn:0199639418

Blue Dreams: The Science and the Story of the Drugs That Changed Our Minds
Lauren Slater, 2018 isbn:0316370649

White Hand Society: The Psychedelic Partnership of Timothy Leary and Allen Ginsberg
Peter Conners, 2010 isbn:0872865754

Food of The Gods: The Search for the Original Tree of Knowledge, A Radical History of Plants, Drugs, and Human Evolution.
Terrence McKenna 1993,

Psilocybin: Magic Mushroom Grower's Guide: A Handbook for Psilocybin Enthusiasts
O.T. Oss, O.N Oeric, 1992 isbn:0932551068

Magic Mushroom Explorer: 'Psilocybin and the Awakening Earth'
Simon G Powell, Rick Doblin, 2015 isbn:1620553678

Mycelium Running: 'How Mushrooms Can Help Save the World'
Paul Stamets, 2005 1580085792

Magic Mushrooms: The Complete Guide to Growing and Using Psilocybin Mushrooms
Richard Korman, isbn:1655014056

#17 - Secret of the Divine Mushrooms
Life Magazine, George Wasson, May 13, 1957

Magic Mushrooms: The Truth About Psilocybin: An Introductory Guide to Shrooms, Psychedelic Mushrooms, and the Full Effects.
Collin Willis, 2015

'John Hopkins Scientists Give Psychedelics the Serious Treatment',
Jan 16, 2020 www.scientificamerican.com

Psilocybin Mushroom Bible
Virginia Haze and Dr. K Mandrake isbn:1937866289

Declassified: Mind Control at McGill
The McGill Tribune, Julie Vanderperre

What We Know About the CIA's Mid-century Mind-Control Project
Smithsonianmag.com, Kat Eschner April 13, 2017

The Long Trip: A Prehistory of Psychedelia
Paul Devereux, 2008

Psychedelics Encyclopedia
Peter Stafford, 1977 isbn:1579511694

The Acid Diaries: 'A Psychonaut's Guide to the History and Use of LSD'
Christopher Gray isbn:9781594773839

The Doors of Perception
Aldous Huxley, 1954 isbn:979-8726003603

Magic Mushrooms
Peter G Stafford 2003, isbn:0914171194

Shroom: A Cultural History of The Magic Mushroom
Andy Letcher, 2006 isbn:0791051838

#18 - The Most Dangerous Man in America: Timothy Leary, Richard Nixon and the Hunt for the Fugitive King of LSD
Bill Minutaglio, 2018 isbn:9781455563586

LSD Psychotherapy
Stanislov Grof, 1994, Hunter House isbn:0897931580

Timothy Leary, The Harvard Years: Early Writings on LSD and Psilocybin
Richard Alpert, Huston Smith, Ralph Metzner and others 2014 isbn:9781620552352

Psychedelic Healing: The Promise of Entheogens for Psychotherapy and Spiritual Development
Neal M Goldsmith, 2011

The Psychedelic Experience: A Manual based on the Tibetan Book of the Dead
Timothy Leary, Ralph Metzner, Richard Alpert isbn:0806516526

The Psychedelic Explorer's Guide: Safe, Therapeutic and Sacred Journeys
James Fadiman PHD. 2011 isbn:1594774021

Plants of the Gods: Their Sacred, Healing and Hallucinogenic Powers
Richard Evans Schultes, Albert Hoffman, and Christian Ratsch

'They Broke My Mental Shackles"
Theguardian.com, June 10, 2019

'Army Misled G.I.'s in Tests of LSD'
NY Times, Joseph Treaster Sept 9, 1975

#3 - 'How Historians Are Reckoning with the Former Nazi Who Launched Americas Space Program'
Time Magazine, 2019 Alejandro De La Garza

Quantum Science of Psychedelics: The Pineal Gland, Multi-Dimensional Reality and Mayan Cosmology
Carl Johan Callemen PH.D 2020

#2 - 'Operation Paperclip – The Secret Intelligence Program That Brought Nazi Scientists to America'
Annie Jacobsen 2014

'Psychedelic Medicine: The Healing Powers of LSD, MDMA, Psilocybin, and Ayahuasca
Richard Louis Miller, 2019

#13 - 'The Whitey Bulger Notebook'
I-Team: Whitey Bulger's Notebook Chronicles LSD Prison Testing, CBS Boston

#14 - 'Point-Saint-Esprit' Poisoning: Did the CIA Spread LSD
BBC News, August 23, 2010

#15 – 'Report Suggests CIA Involvement in FLA Illnesses'
Washington Post, December 17, 1979

#4 – 'Conspiracy Theory in America'
Lance DeHaven-Smith, 2013

#6, #7, 'What Did the CIA Do to His Father'
NY Times, 1970 Michael Ignatieff,

#16 - 'A Brief History of Psychedelic Psychiatry'
The Guardian, Mo Costandi, Sept 5, 2014

#19 – The Electric Kool-Aid Acid Test
Tom Wolfe, August 1968

Reports, Papers and Government Documents:

#1, #5, #8, #9, #10, #13 - **Joint Hearing before the Select Committee Intelligence and the Sub Committee on Health and Scientific Research of the Committee on Human Resources United States Senate**. www.intelligence.senate.gov August 3, 1977

Controlled Drugs and Substances Act (S.C 1996, c19)

United Nations Psychotropic Substances Act of 1978

#20 - **United Nations Convention on Psychotropic Substances 1971**

#21 - **Controlled Substances Act (CSA) of 1970**

U.N. Single Convention on Narcotic Drugs, 1961

Videos:

'Can Magic Mushrooms Unlock Depression?' Rosalind Watts
TEDxOxford TEDxTalks Feb 28, 2017

'The Science of Psilocybin and It's Use to Relieve Suffering'
Roland Griffiths TEDMED TedTalk, April 2016

The Power of Addiction and the Addiction of Power
Dr. Gabor Mate, Tedtalkx20 October 9, 2012

'Optimizing Psilocybin Drug for Clinical Precision'
Psychedelic Science 2017, Albert Garcia-Romeu John Hopkins
University

"CIA, MK Ultra Op, Sandoz LSD 25, Brainwashing Experiments
in the 1960's"
ABC Documentary with Paul Altmeyer, 1970

"MK Ultra"
The Fifth Estate Adrienne Clarkson, CBC News March 11, 1980

#11 – 'Group Affected by CIA Brainwashing'
CBC News. May 22, 2018, Lisa Ellenwood

"Brainwashed: The Echoes of MK-Ultra"
The Fifth Estate, CBC News, October 2020

Websites:

www.doubleblindmag.com – a biannual print magazine and media
company covering, timely untold stories about the expansion of
psychedelics around the globe.

www.adf.org.au – Alcohol and Drug Foundation

www.hopkinsmedicine.org – John Hopkins Center for Psychedelic and
Consciousness Research

Printed in Great Britain
by Amazon

74899990R00102